Carole Ferrier is a Reader in t
Queensland University where
Literature and Women's Studi
she founded *Hecate: An Interc*
Liberation and is still its editor. She has published widely in the area of women's writing.

By Janet Frame from The Women's Press:

Faces in the Water (1980)
Living in the Maniototo (1981)
Scented Gardens for the Blind (1982)
You Are Now Entering the Human Heart (1984)
Owls Do Cry (1985)
An Autobiography (1990)
The Pocket Mirror (1992)

THE JANET FRAME READER

Compiled and edited by Carole Ferrier

First published by The Women's Press Ltd, 1995
A member of the Namara Group
34 Great Sutton Street, London EC1V 0DX

British Library Cataloguing-in-Publication Data
A catalogue record for this book is available from the British Library

ISBN 0 7043 4434 3

This volume may not be sold outside the UK, the EC and EFTA countries.

Phototypeset by Intype, London

Printed and bound in Great Britain by BPC Paperbacks, Aylesbury

contents

Published Works by Janet Frame 7
Preface 11

PART ONE: *MEMORIES* 23

Extracts from
1 *The Lagoon and Other Stories*: 'The Lagoon' 25
2 *To the Is-Land* 28
3 *Owls Do Cry* 30
4 *To the Is-Land* 37
5 *Scented Gardens for the Blind* 41
6 *Intensive Care* 45
7 *An Angel at My Table* 54
8 *Owls Do Cry* 60
9 *A State of Siege* 71
10 *Faces in the Water* 73
11 *Owls Do Cry* 84
12 *The Pocket Mirror*: 'Sunday Drive' 88
13 *The Rainbirds* 93
14 *The Envoy from Mirror City* 98
15 *The Envoy from Mirror City* 103

■ PART TWO: *DREAMS* 113

Extracts from

16 *The Lagoon*: 'The day of the sheep' 115
17 *Snowman, Snowman* 119
18 *Snowman, Snowman* 125
19 *Daughter Buffalo* 133
20 *The Pocket Mirror*: 'The Clock Tower' 138
21 *Living in the Maniototo* 139
22 *A State of Siege* 141
23 *Intensive Care* 147
24 *The Carpathians* 156

■ PART THREE: *REFLECTIONS* 163

Extracts from

25 *The Lagoon*: 'My Last Story' 165
26 *The Adaptable Man* 166
27 *Living in the Maniototo* 168
28 *The Envoy from Mirror City* 176
29 *The Pocket Mirror*: 'Dunedin Story' 188
30 *The Carpathians* 191
31 *Living in the Maniototo* 198
32 *Daughter Buffalo* 200
33 *Intensive Care* 203
34 *The Carpathians* 204

Afterword 207
List of Sources 225
Full Bibliography of the Works of Janet Frame 227
Critical Bibliography 229

PUBLISHED WORKS BY JANET FRAME*

The Lagoon and Other Stories, 1951
Owls Do Cry (novel), 1957
Faces in the Water (novel), 1961
The Edge of the Alphabet (novel), 1961
Scented Gardens for the Blind (novel), 1963
The Reservoir: Stories and Sketches, 1963
Snowman, Snowman: Fables and Fantasies, 1963
The Adaptable Man (novel), 1965
The Reservoir and Other Stories, 1966
A State of Siege (novel), 1966
The Pocket Mirror (poetry), 1968
The Rainbirds (novel), 1968
Mona Minim and the Smell of the Sun (youth fiction), 1969
Intensive Care (novel), 1970
Daughter Buffalo (novel), 1972
Living in the Maniototo (novel), 1979
You Are Now Entering the Human Heart (short stories), 1983
To The Is-Land (Autobiography 1), 1983
An Angel at My Table (Autobiography 2), 1984
The Envoy from Mirror City (Autobiography 3), 1985
The Carpathians (novel), 1988

* dates are of first publication

Preface

Janet Frame's literary output now spans a period of nearly fifty years. She began to produce fiction in the mid-1940s, and her first story was published in 1947. Her writing, in its central preoccupations, its philosophical and political complexity, and its innovative narrative strategies, is both separate from the currents of literature of this period and centrally of them. When Keri Hulme was asked recently about Frame's relationship to recent writing she replied: 'Janet is a stream entire unto herself' (Interview, 1994). At the same time, Frame's work has considerably impressed and influenced other writers; the New Zealand novelist Fiona Kidman tells her: 'You are the presence and the words by which we measure ourselves – and of course, too often, find ourselves wanting' (Alley, 1994, p. 67). For another fellow New Zealand writer, Rosie Scott, who now lives in Australia:

> Some of the things she has written about writing spoke to me in a way that no other 'writing about writing' ever has, and I feel I know completely what she is talking about, and it is confirming for me as a writer to read that. I think she delineates it so honestly and clearly and beautifully; so I have a huge amount of respect for her, and we create in very similar ways it seems to me – it's like meeting a friend to read her.
>
> (Interview, 1992, p. 37)

The New York writer, Barbara Wersba comments:

> With each of her novels a door in my mind opened wider. The books were very readable, yet ahead of their time – the word post-modern could not contain them. They were states of consciousness, interior landscapes, and the prose seemed to catch light, like mirrors.
>
> (Alley, 1994, p. 164)

And the European writer Anna Grazia Mattei said:

> There is an incessant challenge, rewarding even when baffling, to enter into a dialogue with this extraordinary writer – an everlasting observer and explorer of the real and the visible, engaged in a constant search for its hidden dimension, the 'life within', and for a new form to convey it.
>
> (Alley, p. 176)

Mattei pointed out that Frame's work played a crucial part in 'decolonising our European metropolitan minds by opening them up to dynamic cross-cultural encounters'. Cross-cultural encounter is discussed in detail by Frame herself as a dialectical process in which there may be 'a dominance, a submission, a merging or a resistance'. ('Departures and Returns', in Amirthanagayam, ed, 1982, p. 91.) At the same time, she suggests, direct influences cannot always be simply attributed: 'At the edge of awareness, cultures, like the planets and stars, have inexplicable or explicable moon-bursts, sun and star-bursts, and sometimes feed, one literature into another, where there has been no traceable contact.' ('Departures and Returns', p. 93.) The closeness in many respects of Frame's writing to that of Doris Lessing, for example, in the use both make of the metaphors of the mental traveller and the dream city, may be of this order.

A striking feature of Frame's fiction is that a great deal of it can be read as being 'writing about writing'. It is pervasively self-reflexive, often metafictional – that is, fiction that talks about *being* fiction, that considers constantly the process and contexts of its creation. It is writing that searches for clarity of insight – but insight that can only be expressed through words that are slippery, that 'wriggle' ('Beginnings', 1965, p. 42) when they are grasped and which, in everyday discourse, often camouflage rather than clarify. It is writing that expresses a profound, almost overpowering desire to push language to the limits of its effective use, moving apparently effortlessly through different registers. Take the depth and complexity of this apparently simple passage from one of her first stories:

> My aunt drew aside the curtain and peered out. She reminded me of the women in films who turn to the window in an emotional moment, but the moment wasn't emotional nor was my aunt.
> —It's an interesting story, she said. I prefer Dostoevsky to Truth.
> ('The Lagoon', see p. 27)

Intensity, lively intelligence and profundity, embodied in the most careful possible choice of words is the hallmark of all her work. Gina Mercer in her recent book on Frame (one of the most substantial and interesting commentaries to date) suggests:

> she is in love with language but, realizing its power, sees the necessity to make war on it. To bring about change she feels there must be an effort to split the alphabetical atom, to explode the current construction of language to create something new.
> (Mercer, 1994, p. 167)

* * *

Janet Frame was born in 1924 in Dunedin in the South Island of New Zealand. She grew up in Oamaru (the Waimaru of her first published novel, *Owls Do Cry*), and later attended Dunedin Teachers' Training College and Otago University. Experiencing an increasing sense of difference and alienation, she reports that one day when the Inspector was visiting her class at school she said ' "Will you excuse me a moment please?" . . . I walked out of the room and out of the school, knowing I would never return.' (*An Autobiography*, 1989, p. 187.) For about ten years from 1945, interspersed with attempts to support herself financially through working as a waitress and housemaid, she spent long periods in three psychiatric hospitals (much of this experience finding parallels with that narrated in her second published novel, *Faces in the Water*, and where she was given treatment that produced the effect of feeling 'stopped like a house to look forever on its backyard' (*Owls Do Cry*, see p. 84). According to her autobiography *An Angel at My Table*, she avoided a leucotomy only because one of the doctors had seen in the newspaper that she had won a prize for her first book, *The Lagoon and Other Stories*, and announced: 'I've decided that you should stay as you are. I don't want you changed' (*Angel*, 1984, p. 111). Years later, in London, she was to be told 'I should never have been admitted to a mental hospital. Any problems I now experienced were mostly a direct result' (*Envoy*, see pp. 185–6).

Becoming a writer was, for Frame, the aim of her life from early on and, almost literally, a matter of life and death. It was with much struggle that she achieved it, drawing always upon 'memory, and a pocketful of words' ('Memory and a Pocketful of Words', 1964, p. 487), along with 'designs from . . . dreams' ('Beginnings', p. 46). The publication of *The Lagoon and Other Stories* was an encouragement in her search for the writer's identity she needed to be able to assume, in order to be able to validate a vision that tended to express itself in a 'conflagration' of comforting clichés (*A State of Siege*, New York, 1966, p. 116). She was also heartened by the acceptance of some of her work by journal editors. But passing through Christchurch during one of her periods of discharge from the hospitals, she found in the local newspaper, the *Press*, a review 'that dismissed *The Lagoon and Other Stories* with phrases like "This kind of thing has been done before too often" . . . I felt painful humiliation and rejection, an increased torment of not knowing where *to be* – if I could not live within the world of writing books, then where could I survive' (*Angel*, p. 103). Her fellow writer, Frank Sargeson, was an important influence in the early 1950s, providing material support, a place to stay and meals. She reports the feeling of release produced by 'the prospect of living as a writer, with a place to work, to be alone, with no worry over money, and sharing meals and company with someone who actually *believed* I was a writer' (*Angel*, p. 142). Sargeson also helped her to gain the confidence to make a break, for several years, from a New Zealand environment that had become too known and *knowing*, although to leave and travel posed the question of how to retain connections, roots:

> The lemon tree has shallow roots and the roots of the fig tree go deep. The lemon tree's roots are easily flooded, too, and decay easily; while the fig tree can invade territory where it's not welcome and then it is cut down, killed in spite of its fruit. Though often new leaves start years later from the apparently dead tree.
>
> ('Departures', p. 91)

Later, the remembered happiness at Sargeson's and his contribution to her managing to get her first novel published makes Margaret Rose Hurndell, the exiled writer, a kind of alter ego. The writer Frame describes as visiting her villa at Menton encounters 'an air of desolation in the room and beyond it . . . The chill, of the wind and of the spirit' (*Living in the Maniototo*, see pp. 172–3). Nonetheless, despite the sound of the 'grass swaying in the neglected garden, and the brittle rustling of flax bush', the flax 'that a sympathetic writer had planted near the crumbling wall' has the quality of life later attributed to it by Rua in *The Carpathians* (see p. 197); it is now 'a mass of soaring green spears' (*Maniototo*, see p. 173).

Frame's sense of alienation, both personal and literary, within New Zealand society was undoubtedly compounded by being female. Several other New Zealand women writers were labelled 'mad', and incarcerated, notably Eve Langley and Robin Hyde. Others left to go overseas, in search of wider scope, including Jean Devanny. In *Where Did She Come From* (1989), Heather Roberts constructed a 'female tradition' of New Zealand women writers, but Frame fits in some senses uneasily into this pattern and there is a lot more room for in-depth study to be done in this field. Frame does, however, pay tribute to feminism, suggesting that it contributed in her lifetime to an improvement in the condition of the writer, through challenging an outsider status that functioned as primarily destructive: 'I think artists are no longer looked on as strangers, trespassers, and I feel that partly we must thank the women's movement for the acceptance of artists' (McLeod, Interview, 1988, p. 25). When Gina Mercer asked in an interview how she felt about being taken up by feminists, she responded: 'They have converted me . . . I'd often thought about my mother in relation to other women and women of that time with their housework all day and so on, and their not being able to develop their creative side' (Mercer, 1994, p. 237).

Powerfully communicated in much of her earlier work is the sense of the impossibility of a young woman's escape from the imposition of femininity, generated by those institutions involved in the reproduction and control of New Zealand society – the family and the asylum in particular. A self-perception of difference or otherness – embodied for example in the story told in *An Angel at My Table* of the skirt with the appliquéd giraffe that is viewed as eccentric and excessive – or a perception of people being enclosed in bell jars, 'separately sealed worlds, like glass globes of trick snowstorms' (*Faces*, see p. 81) becomes, as time goes on, an indicator of pathology for those who have power over her. She is punished for being other, and any avenues of escape disappear.

> Faced with the family anguish I made my usual escape, the route now perfected, and once again I was in Seacliff hospital. I knew as soon as I arrived there that the days of practising that form of escape were over. I would go away somewhere, live on my own, earn enough money to live on, write my books: it was no use: I now had what was known as a 'history', and ways of dealing with those with a 'history' were stereotyped, without investigation . . . The state could be defined as forced submission to custodial capture.
>
> (*Angel*, pp. 108–9)

* * *

An aspect of the intellectual challenge of Frame's work is its frequent anticipation of particular contemporary schools of thought that have often, in their other articulations, produced much highly complicated, even opaque theorisation. Her depiction of 'madness' in *Owls Do Cry* and subsequent texts prefigures, for example, the development of Laingian anti-psychiatry from the late 1950s, which worked with a notion of 'schizophrenia' as being in a state of consciousness that operates on 'another order of reality akin to a waking dream'. Her critiques of the sexual politics of the family (like those in the earlier novels of Doris Lessing and Christina Stead) predate the development of second wave feminism, while Betty Friedan's 1963 analysis of the 'feminine mystique' and 'the problem that had no name' is anticipated by Frame's representations of the domestic lives of women 'muddling backwards and forwards in little irrelevant journeys but going backwards always. ('The Day of the Sheep', *Lagoon*, see p. 118). Her picture of the persisting impact on 'private' life of the extensive participation of New Zealand men in what are sometimes called the theatres of the First and Second World Wars – chillingly shown in the gasmasked father acting out a 'private performance' of the bayoneting of an effigy of Guy Fawkes (*Intensive Care*, see p. 50) – while recalling the images of 'shell-shock' in novels like Virginia Woolf's *Mrs Dalloway*, also connects up with recent feminist critiques of the impact of imperialism and militarism upon family life. The discipline maintained over individuals by institutions, through a variety of means ranging from physical force to language (for example, using words to 'label' or stigmatise) is another frequently recurring theme. The ways in which social control is produced are recapitulated in various ways through her writing, finding parallels with one central concern of recent critical theory – how power is exercised through language. Trinh T Minh-ha has suggested:

> Power, as unveiled by numerous contemporary writings, has always inscribed itself in language. Speaking, writing and discoursing are not mere acts of communication; they are above all acts of compulsion . . . The attempt to impose a human reality onto an inexplicably different world is as obvious, as tangible as language can be in its crude being.
>
> (Minh-ha, 1989, 112)

Frame's pervasive playing with language foreshadows poststructuralism's concerns with the indeterminacy of meaning. (I have reviewed the debates in recent critical work on Frame about whether she can be called 'modernist', 'postmodernist' or something in between, in Ferrier, 1994.) Her 'imposter' or mystery narrators and multiple levels of narration, exemplified most explicitly in her (at the time of writing) most recent novel, *The Carpathians*, parallel the Barthesian and Foucauldian questioning of 'authority', how one can obtain the ability to speak, and to speak against the dominant discourses. In earlier texts like *Owls Do Cry* and *Intensive Care* this speaking against was carried out partly through highly skilled humorous parody of women's magazines (see pp. 45–54 and 60–71).

* * *

In many ways Frame is an international author; initially removed into exile from her society through forcible institutionalisation, she subsequently travelled overseas seeking freedom from configurations into which she had been forced – although, as D H Lawrence put it: 'You've always got yourself on your hands in the end.' These earlier experiences contributed to the state of mind that she reports in 'Departures and Returns' in 1982: 'I have no backyard. I have lost it in a cross-cultural encounter, both of space and time' (p. 91). She spent some time in Europe and the United States, several of her books being set there, and several of the narrator protagonists in her fiction journey to or from the States. Her novels have received many literary prizes and been translated into German (from as early as 1961), Dutch, French, Italian and Spanish. Those from early in her career have been generally favoured for translation, though part of the autobiography has also, and a couple of her stories have been rendered into Russian. The bibliography in Jeanne Delbaere's anthology of critical articles on Frame's work, *The Ring of Fire*, demonstrates that there is now widespread interest in her writing, though there are still few monographs. However, Delbaere suggests in her introduction:

> Though she is beginning to receive more and more attention all over the world, Janet Frame is still waiting for the audience she deserves, partly because most of her novels have been out of print for some

> time, partly because she is, even by contemporary standards, a difficult novelist.
>
> (Delbaere, 1992, p. 13)

Frame has now published more than twenty books; half of these are fiction, and the remainder are volumes of short fiction, youth fiction, poetry and autobiography. (The bibliography on pages 227–28 gives a full list.) They have been perceived as crossing the boundaries of genres and forms; she herself comments in an interview: 'My novels are not novels. I wanted to call them explorations' (Dowrick, 45). Gina Mercer has suggested, 'One of the most fixed and impassible borders in literature is between poetry and prose yet Janet Frame repeatedly traverses this border, writing poetic prose and including whole chapters of poetry in her fictional explorations' (Mercer, 1985). Perhaps Mercer's first point about impassibility is overstated if we think of other writers such as Virginia Woolf or Gertrude Stein who have done something similar. But it *is* certainly the case that what often looks like naïve (even artless) simplicity is usually a very dense and poetic prose, whose recycling or reconceptualisation of the mythmaking that is literature explodes kaleidoscopically along the lines described by Lévi-Strauss:

> Just when you think you have disentangled and separated them, you realise that they are knitting together again in response to the operation of unexpected affinities. Consequently the unity of myth is never more than tendential and projective . . . It is a phenomenon of the imagination, resulting from the attempt at interpretation.
>
> (Lévi-Strauss, 1969, p. 5)

Frame's fiction has been described by C K Stead as a 'mixed genre' (1981, p. 130); my selection from her work further combines the various 'genres' into which her writing might be categorised – prose fiction, poetry, autobiography, the essay and the interview – producing some considerable shifts of narrative voice within the total text. The tone of the essay or of the autobiography is often a distinctively different one to the voice of fiction or poetry – sometimes implying more *explanation* as opposed to the ambiguous suggestion that tends to be the dominant tone of explicitly 'fictional' writing, sometimes purporting to offer more direct access to the author's view. Frame's own – constructed – subjectivity within her texts has often been read too literally by critics of her work who have, for example, tended to interpret her autobiography in a rather shallow way as allowing the nearest access to the 'truth' about her life.

Hence, there are some difficulties in offering as my Preface to this selection something that might be perceived as having elements of biographical sketch, intersecting with or drawing upon her own three volumes labelled autobiography. What Carl Jung said in 1957 is relevant here:

> When we are old we are drawn back, both from within and without, to memories of youth . . . During the last years the suggestion has come to me from various quarters that I should do something akin to an autobiography. I have been unable to conceive of my doing anything of the sort. I know too many autobiographies, with their self-deception and downright lies, and I know too much about the impossibility of self-portrayal, to want to venture on any such attempt.
>
> (*Memories, Dreams, Reflections*, viii)

It *is* valuable for Frame's work to be placed in the context of its own time and place, so that its historical determinants and influences can be perceived. Nonetheless, it is important not to fall into an unreflective notion of the 'truth to (her) life' of the narratives offered by commentators who draw on apparently autobiographical information, or on her three volumes of autobiography (*To the Is-Land, An Angel at My Table, The Envoy from Mirror City*). Even more problematically, some commentators have read the novels themselves as straightforwardly autobiographical. Frame expresses her own concern about to what this can lead, giving a graphic instance in relation to *Owls Do Cry*:

> I was alarmed to find that it was believed to be autobiographical, with the characters actual members of my family, and myself the

> character Daphne upon whom a brain operation was performed. Confronted by a doctor who had read the book, I was obliged to demonstrate to him the absence of leucotomy scars on my temples. Not every aspiring writer has such a terrifying but convincing method of displaying to others 'proof' that she has been writing fiction.
>
> (*Angel*, pp. 148–49)

Later she was to say:

> I have never written directly of my own life and feelings. Undoubtedly I have mixed myself with other characters who themselves are a product of known and unknown, real and imagined; I have created 'selves'; but I have never written of 'me'.
>
> (*Envoy*, London, 1985, p. 140)

Jane Campion's film *An Angel at My Table* has also often been read as Frame's life (his)story, and perhaps asks to be read this way. It seems to make the figure of Frame familiar and accessible. Of course, this is positive in one sense if it produces more readers for her work. Apart, however, from the difficulties drawn attention to by Jung, and by Frame herself, in making an identification between the textual self and the author's 'real' self, the film also had other problems to circumvent, the main one being summed up by Marion McLeod as 'how to translate a work about words, about writing – where language is the main character – into a visual medium' (McLeod, 1990, p. 102). Perhaps it is better to read the film not as the 'true' story of Frame's life, but as a parallel text that brings out, through what it (as a film text) cannot do, the linguistic richness on the page of Frame's texts.

What *can* perhaps be drawn from such details of a real or imagined life, however, is a representation of how a particular outsider is dealt with in a particular culture, as well as 'the genesis of the artist as the novelist conceives her', as W B Broughton puts it (227). While I do not wish to place too much emphasis upon a notion of *development* – of artistic and personal evolution – particular preoccupations *do* surface periodically in both the personal and the writing life, expressed through recurring images that flow between and across the texts. Accordingly, rather than using a too simplistically autobiographical or developmental structure, I have grouped the pieces I have chosen to include into three sections: Memories, Dreams, and Reflections. Having chosen certain excerpts and not others, and having chosen to order them in a certain way, I cannot avoid encouraging particular readings of Frame's writing; the way I have grouped them, however, is also intended to produce a blurring and overlapping of patterns as certain preoccupations ebb and flow in the different tidal configurations of the texts and their various currents. This method signals its recognition of Frame's own complex methods of linguistic play, that mobilise allegory, metaphor and metonymy, and a kaleidoscopic pattern of symbolic meanings. Every word matters enormously to Janet Frame. One of the main challenges posed to anyone who tries to talk about her work is to use words with anything approaching her competence, to build a craft that can navigate her ocean of story. In the Afterword that follows Frame's text, I discuss some of the questions that her work has been seen as posing for readers and critics, and poses for me.

PART ONE

memories

It seems impossible and unreal, but the reality of the feeling fills the memory to the brim even though the time is out of reach.

(*Living in the Maniototo*, p. 53)

Memory is a subversive force allied to strong feeling.

(*A State of Siege*, p. 69)

I must not dream thus. I dread going to Waimaru. The world of childhood widens with every wish of the child that it may be worn like a magic cloak about the shoulder. I shall return to Waimaru and find it, like the skin of the wild ass, shrivelling at my every desire, a shrunken scrap of wrinkle between my thumb and forefinger.

(*Owls Do Cry*, p. 135)

1.

At low tide the water is sucked back into the harbour and there is no lagoon, only a stretch of dirty grey sand shaded with dark pools of sea-water where you may find a baby octopus if you are lucky, or the spotted orange old house of a crab or the drowned wreckage of a child's toy boat. There is a bridge over the lagoon where you may look down into the little pools and see your image tangled up with sea-water and rushes and bits of cloud. And sometimes at night there is an under-water moon, dim and secret.

All this my grandmother told me, my Picton grandmother who could cut supple jack and find kidney fern and make a track through the thickest part of the bush. When my grandmother died all the Maoris at the Pa came to her funeral, for she was a friend of the Maoris, and her mother had been a Maori princess, very beautiful they said, with fierce ways of loving and hating.

See the lagoon, my grandmother would say. The dirty lagoon, full of drifting wood and sea-weed and crabs' claws. It is dirty and sandy and smelly in summer. I remember we used to skim round white stones over the water, and catch tiddlers in the little creek near by, and make sand castles on the edge, this is my castle we said, you be father I'll be mother and we'll live here and catch crabs and tiddlers for ever.

I liked my grandmother to talk about the lagoon. And when we went for a holiday to Picton where grandma lived I used to say grandma tell me a story. About the Maori Pa. About the old man who lived down the Sounds and had a goat and a cow for friends. About the lagoon. And my grandmother would tell me stories of the Sounds and the Pa and herself when she was young. Being a girl and going out to work in the rich people's houses. But the lagoon never had a proper story, or if it had a proper story my grandmother never told me.

See the water she would say. Full of sea-weed and crabs' claws. But I knew that wasn't the real story and I didn't find out the real story till I was grown-up and grandma had died and most of the old Maoris were gone from the Pa, and the old man and the cow and the goat were forgotten.

I went for a holiday in Picton. It was a long journey by train and I was glad at the end of it to see the green and blue town that I remembered from childhood, though it was smaller of course and the trees had shrunk and the hills were tiny.

I stayed with an aunt and uncle. I went for launch rides round the harbour and I went for picnics with summery people in floral frocks and sun hats, and kids in print frocks, or khaki shorts if they were boys, especially if they were boys with fathers in the army. We took baskets with fruit and sandwiches, not tomato for tomato goes damp though some like it damp, and threepences in the pocket for ice-creams. There were races for the kiddies and some for the men and women, and afterwards a man walked round the grounds throwing lollies in the air. They were great days out picnicking in the Sounds with the Maoris singing and playing their ukeleles, but they didn't sing the real Maori songs, they sang You are my sunshine and South of the Border. And then it got dark and the couples came back from the trees and the launches were got ready and everybody went back singing, with the babies crying because they were tired and sunburnt and bitten by sandflies. Sandflies are the devil everybody said, but they were great days they were great days for the kiddies.

Perhaps I liked the new Picton, I don't know. If there were things I hadn't noticed before there were also things gone that I thought would be there for ever. The two gum trees that I called the two ladies were gone or if they were there I couldn't find them, and the track over the Domain Hill wasn't there. We used to climb up and watch the steamer coming in from the straits. And there was gorse mixed up with the bush, and the bush itself didn't hold the same fear, even with its secret terrible drippings and rustlings that go on for ever.

There were more people in the town too. The Main Trunk Line brings more tourists, my aunt said. There were people everywhere, lying on the beach being burned or browned by the sun and sea, people whizzing round the harbour in motorboats like the pop-pop boats we used to whizz round in the bath on Christmas morning. People surf-riding, playing tennis, fishing in the Straits, practising in skiffs for the Regatta. People.

But my grandmother wasn't there to show me everything and tell me stories. And the Lagoon was dirtier than ever. See the lagoon said my aunt. Full of drifting wood and sea-weed and crabs' claws. We could see the lagoon from the kitchen window. We were looking at photographs that day, what silly clothes people wore in those days. There was grandma sitting on the verandah with her knitting, and there was my great grandmother, the Maori princess with her big brown eyes, and her lace dress on that her husband bought her, handmade lace said my aunt, he loved her till he met that woman from Nelson, men are crazy sometimes, but I suppose women are crazier.

—Is there a story, I said. I was a child again, grandma tell me about . . .

My aunt smiled. She guesses things sometimes.

—The sort of story they put in Truth, she said. On the morning of the tragedy witness saw defendant etc. etc. Your great grandmother was a murderess. She drowned her husband, pushed him in the lagoon. I suppose the tide was high, I don't know. They would call it The Woman From Nelson . . . she mused. They would have photos. But then nobody knew, only the family. Everybody thought he had had one over the eight and didn't know where he was going.

My aunt drew aside the curtain and peered out. She reminded me of the women in films who turn to the window in an emotional moment, but the moment wasn't emotional nor was my aunt.

—It's an interesting story, she said. I prefer Dostoevsky to Truth.

The water was brown and shining and to the right lay the dark shadow of the Domain Hill. There were kids playing on the edge, Christopher Robins with sand between the toes, sailing toy warships and paddling with bare feet in the pools.

—Grandmother never told me, I said.

Again my aunt smiled. The reason (she quoted) one talks farthest from the heart is the fear that it may be hurt.

And then my aunt dropped the curtain across the window and turned to the photographs again.

Was it my aunt speaking or was it my grandmother or my great grandmother who loved a white lace dress?

At low tide there is no lagoon. Only a stretch of dirty grey sand. I remember we used to skim thin white stones over the water and catch tiddlers in the little creek near by and make sand castles, this is my castle we said you be father I'll be mother and we'll live here and catch crabs and tiddlers for ever . . .

2.

Something new, a silent time of deeper thinking, had entered my life, and I associate it with those afternoons of silent reading, the very name of the activity puzzling me, when the silence was so full of inner noise that I could not make myself interested in the Whitcombes Readers. We were 'on to' Pinocchio; I thought it was a stupid story. I thought Don Quixote was a fool. I sat doing nothing on those dreary afternoons, full of thinking yet not knowing what I was thinking, watching the beams of dust, whitened with chalk, floating around in the window light and knowing that I used to think they were sunbeams.

Then, one afternoon, when we had singing from the Dominion Song book, a class I loved, we sang a haunting song, 'Like to the tide moaning in grief by the shore,/ mourn I for friends captured and warriors slain . . .' We sang the Maori words, too: E pare ra . . . As we were singing, I felt suddenly that I was crying because something terrible had happened, although I could not say what it was: it was inside the song, yet outside it, with me. When school was over, I ran home, even passing some of the big boys at Hunt's Corner, and when I reached the gate, I was out of breath. I came around the corner into the back yard. Myrtle was standing there. 'The Old Cat is dead,' she said abruptly.

We buried the Old Cat in the garden. She had been black and fluffy, and when she grew old, her fur grew brown as if it had been scorched. Since we had lived in Oamaru, cats and their kittens had arrived from nowhere to live with us and there was a special place in the washhouse near the copper were they always had their kittens. Although we were never allowed to have the cats inside, we sometimes sneaked them in when Dad was at work, and we were close to them in their births and deaths. We did not then each have an animal. Myrtle's Old Cat was shared with all, and it was now unthinkable that another animal would not arrive to take the place of Old Cat.

The sad afternoon of the singing of 'E pare ra' became part of my memories, like the wind in the telegraph wires and the discovery of My Place. I thought it was strange that we could be singing of 'friends captured and warriors slain' while I could be seeing in my mind the lonely beach with the tide 'moaning in grief by the shore' and people on the beach who were the people in the song, the warriors, and others who were Myrtle, Bruddie, and I at Waipapa or Fortrose; yet at the same time I could be feeling a dread and unhappiness that I could not name, which had little relation to this song, and still at the same time be sitting in the brown classroom, watching the dust travelling in and out of the beams of light slanting through the windows that were so tall that the monitors had to struggle each morning to open them, using ropes and levers and a long pole with a hook on the end; all school windows were thus, constantly at war with being opened or shut. And when Myrtle said, 'Old Cat's dead,' I knew it already; yet it was something else, too, as well as Old Cat.

About two weeks later Myrtle arrived home from school with Lassie, the spaniel dog, which had quite naturally followed her. Well, Lassie was a bitch because she was fat with rows of titties, but we were forbidden to say the word *bitch*. In spite of arguments and threats from Dad and talk of hydatids from Mum, we kept Lassie and two of the pups that were born the following week. The others were tied in a sugar bag with a stone to weigh them down and drowned in the creek. Gradually over the years, the bed of the creek became the resting place of many cats, kittens, pups, not only from us but from neighbours, with now and then, when the sack rotted, a wet cat shape with teeth set in a skeleton snarl, rising to the surface.

3.

It was an afternoon in a hall filled with people, girls in their white spun silk, each holding shilling bags of coconut ice, pink and white, from the home-made sweet stall; mothers who smelled like a closed room of talcum powder and stored fur; with their parcels from the handwork sale, tablerunners and tea-showers in lazy-daisy and chain and shadow stitch.

It was the last day of the term and Francie's last day at school though she was only twelve, thirteen after Christmas. She could count up to thirty in French. She could make puff pastry, dabbing the butter carefully before each fold. She could cook sago, lemon or pink with cochineal, that swelled in cooking from dirty little grains, same, same, dusty and bagged in paper, to lemon or pink pears. She knew that a drop of iodine on a slice of banana will blacken the fruit, and prove starch; that water is H_2O; that a man called Shakespeare, in a wood near Athens, contrived a moonlit dream.

But in all her knowing, she had not learned the time of living, the unseen always, when people are like the marbles in the fun alley at the show; and a gaudy circumstance will squeeze payment from their cringing and poverty-stricken fate, to give him the privilege of rolling them into the bright or dark box, till they drop into one of the little painted holes, their niche, it is called, and there roll their lives round and round in a frustrating circle.

And Francie was taken, on the afternoon of the play, like one of the marbles, though still in her silver helmet and breastplate and waiting to be burned; and rolled to a new place beyond Frère Jacques and participles and science and bunsen burners and Shakespeare, there I couch when owls do cry, when owls do cry when owls do cry,

To a new place of bright or dark, of home again, and Mum and Dad and Toby and Chicks; an all-day Mum and Dad, as if she were small again, not quite five, with no school, no school ever, and her world, like her tooth, under her pillow with a promise of sixpence and no school ever any more. No black stockings to buy and get on tick with panama hat and blouse and black shoes, with the salesman spearing the account sheets in a terrible, endless ritual, licking the end of the pencil that is chained by a worn gold chain to the counter, carefully writing the prices, totting the account in larger than ordinary figures so as to see and make quite sure, for the Withers are not going to pay yet. It is all on appro. With the deliberation of power then, the salesman plunges the sheet of paper through the metal spear that stands rooted in a small square of wood; then he moves the wood carefully aside, with the paper speared and torn but spouting no visible blood, and the total unharmed and large, and Francie (or Daphne or Toby or Chicks) staring sideways, afraid, at the committed debt. The Withers are under sentence. It is likely they will be put in prison. And the salesman smooths the sheet of account slips with the power of judgment and fate in the pressure of his hand.

—Will it be all right, the children ask, till the end of the month?

—Certainly, till the end of the month.

But rooted in his mind is the shining awl, the spear to pierce sheaves of accounts and secure them till their day of judgment, to the Last Trump, when the dead spring up like tall boards out of their grave.

But how shall there be room for the dead? They shall be packed tight and thin like malt biscuits or like the pink ones with icing in between that the Withers could never afford; except for Aunty Nettie passing through on the train.

So for Francie now, no black stockings to find and darn or uniform to sponge or panama hat to be cleaned with whiting and water and the time saying, Will you walk a little faster? And the marks are not coming off, and Francie crying because Miss Legget inspected the hats and pointed to the ones not clean and floppy and said,

—A disgrace. Now quick march, girls, toes meet the floor first, quick march, but not Francie Withers.

Francie Withers is dirty. Francie Withers is poor. The Withers haven't a week-end bach nor do they live on the South Hill nor have they got a vacuum cleaner nor do they learn dancing or the piano nor have birthday parties nor their photos taken at the Dainty Studio to be put in the window on a Friday.

Francie Withers has a brother who's a shingle short. She couldn't bring the fuji silk for sewing, she had to bring ordinary boiling silk that you shoot peas through, because she's poor. You never see her mother dressed up. They haven't any clothes and Francie hasn't any shoes for changing to at drill time, and her pants are not *real* black Italian cloth.

She hasn't a school blazer with a monogram.

But Francie Withers is Joan of Arc, and she sang at the garden party—

> Where the bee sucks there suck I
> In a cowslip's bell I lie,
> There I couch when owls do cry.
> When owls do cry, when owls do cry.

But not any more there I couch when owls do cry. There are owls in the macrocarpa and cabbage trees and they cry quee-will, quee-will, and sometimes at night because of the trees you think it is raining for ever and there will be no more sun, only quee-will and dark.

But the day, for Francie, left school, will be forever, with them all having breakfast and their father going to work, smelling of tobacco and shaving soap and the powder he sprinkles on his feet to stop them from becoming athletic.

—What shift, Bob?

—Late shift, Amy. Home at ten.

But very often he did not call her Amy, only Mother, or Mum, as if she really were his mother.

And she would call him Father, or Dad, as if in marrying him she had found another father.

Besides Francie's grandad.

And besides God.

—Yes, late shift, Amy. Home at ten.

—Oh Dad, you'll never get your sleep in.

—If I'm off tomorrow I'll fix the waste pipe.

—It needs fixing.

—Of course it needs fixing. Haven't I told you time and again not to put grease and stuff down it?

—I've been emptying the dishwater outside, on the roses, to keep the blight away.

—You didn't last night.

—I forgot, Dad.

—Good Lord, is that the time? Make sure you keep those kids away from that rubbish dump, they're the talk of the town, them going and playing in all that rubbish, strikes me they can't tell what's rubbish from what isn't rubbish.

—Yes, Dad.

He almost kisses his wife, then, and is gone, wheeling his bike around the corner, and Amy stands looking after him. She wipes her hands on her wet apron, it is always wet, a wide patch of wet where she leans over the sink to wash the dishes.

She thinks for one moment, because she is romantic, of herself and Bob and the time he courted her and sang to her, what was the song—

Come for a trip in my airship
come for a trip midst the stars,
come for a spin around Venus
come for a trip around Mars;
no one to watch while we're kissing,
no one to see while we spoon
Come for a trip in my airship
and we'll visit the man in the moon.

And when they walked down Waikawa Valley, as close to the moon as possible, they met the old Maori running from the ghosts and he called out, Goodnight Miss Hefflin, only he said it like Heaven, and she laughed.

Perhaps Amy thinks for a moment of this, or is it only in books, where cried-for moons are captured, that they think this way?

And then the children are off to school and the littlest one plays in the backyard, that's Chicks, chicken because she's so small and dark; and Francie's there, who's not small but twelve, thirteen after Christmas, but left school now to make her way in the world and get on.

And be part of the day that is forever.

And it is quiet now for Francie. She thinks, now the girls at school will marching in for prayers. A new term has begun. The headmistress will be standing on the platform and raise her hand, not for silence because it is hushed already but because she likes to raise her hand that way. She is big, with a head shaped like a bull and no neck to speak of and you can never see what she is wearing under her gown because it wraps her close like a secret. She is standing, in majesty, before the school and saying Good Morning, girls.

And then it is the National Anthem and the headmistress welcomes everybody for a new term, singing with them, or opening her mouth like singing,

Lord Behold us with thy blessing
once again assembled here
onward be our footsteps pressing
in thy love and faith and fear
still protect us still protect us
by thy presence ever near.

—The Lord, the headmistress says, after the Amen, is very very close.

And she wraps her gown more secretly about her body.

She opens the Bible then, and reads about the Sermon on the Mount.

—And seeing the multitudes he went up into a mountain.

—And, she says the Beatitudes. Blessed are the peacemakers and those that are poor in spirit and those that mourn, and how Christ taught them, saying.

They repeat then, the Lords Prayer, not looking, with a special word added in case there is War, to make the soldiers not afraid; and they sing a long hymn, conducted by the music mistress who is deaf and lipreads and is related to Beethoven; and the hymn has so many verses that if it is a hot day some of the girls faint or have to walk out into the cool air and are able to boast about it afterwards,

—I fainted. I walked out of Assembly, when they sang the long hymn.

O give me Samuel's ear, they sing. His watch the little child the little Levite kept. A real watch, a ticking kind that slices and doles out day like best cake, or the looking watch that you live, sitting your life in a dark house like a box, in case an enemy should come?

It is a sad hymn, the little Levite one, and some of the girls, even the ones with two-storied homes and cars and caravans, will cry; yet when it is finished everything is school again, and the headmistress not any nearer to God; as if there had been no Bible or Jesus going up to the mountain where the air is cool, tasting of snowgrass that grows all the way up; and He passes a dead sheep that the hawks have eaten, and some live sheep sitting side-saddle upon the grass and chewing their cud. And it is a most beautiful mountain out of geography, a Southern Alp, but lessons never teach you how to write it; you only make shading like featherstitch.

So it is all gone in a cloud, and the headmistress is crossing her gown over her bosom and saying

—Girls, there were a number of navy coats and panama hats left at the end of last term. If no one claims them they shall be given to the Chinese Relief Fund.

—Girls, some of you have been seen in the street and not wearing gloves, or talking on corners to the boys from the High School. Girls, girls.

The headmistress is very stern.

The Invercargill March then, and soon the hall is empty.

And Francie is at home caught in a forever morning where every sound is loud and strange. The kitchen clock, the old one that belonged to her grandfather, ticks with a nobbly loudness, staring with its blank dark eye where you put the key to wind it. The front of the clock opens and inside are kept for safety, receipts and bills, art union tickets, and all things that must never be lost or the Withers will be up before the court or bankrupt.

Yet the clock is time, and time is lost, is bankrupt before it begins.

Francie sits in the kitchen. The fire burns with a hissing sound, then a roar until the damper is put in. Sometimes the coal makes a pop-pop.

—It's the gas, Mrs Withers explains. The coal we buy never has it, only the coal your father gets from work.

—Does he pay for it?

—No, Francie, he just brings home what we need.

The forever morning has a bird outside on the plum tree, a dog barking, the voice of the baker calling on the next door neighbour and saying,

—Did you get your bread at the weekend?

and the words seep through the holly hedge, are pricked on the way, come dropping through the kitchen window, firm and red words like holly berries and smelling like bread and primroses and the inside of a teapot.

And why, it *is* teatime, morning tea, and Mrs Withers is sitting spread out on the bin by the fire and drinking tea, with a homemade biscuit leaning wet to the waist in the saucer; and the tide rises and drowns the biscuit and she rescues it, though some of the soggy parts drop on the floor, and she dunks the remains in her tea. And the fairy ring of criss-cross that she made around the edge with an old knitting needle, for decoration, is crumbled away.

And still lunch time does not come. The world is stuck and over and over like a burning spinning and hurt record, and the world is empty, a blue and white sack, hollow, with no people in it, save Mrs Withers and Chicks in a far corner

and the sack gets filled with a bird on the plum tree, and the baker saying

—Did you get your bread at the weekend?

and the clock making a stifling ticking that hops round and round droning, like a swarm, in the sack, and is never let free.

4.

One day I found a friend, Poppy, whose real name was Marjorie. She had lank brown hair, an ugly face with a wide red mouth, and her father whipped her with a narrow machine belt, which made cuts in her skin. Everything she said and did was new to me, even the way she talked and the words she used, her ideas and games and the folklore that I didn't think of as folklore but as truth rumours passed from one person to another. Poppy taught me how to cure warts by squeezing the juice of the ice plant over them. We'd sit on the Glen Street clay bank that was covered with purple-flowering ice plant, and we'd wriggle as the stems of the ice plant dug into our bottoms, and we'd squeeze the juice of the stems over our warts, and, miraculously, within a few days our warts disappeared. Poppy taught me how to suck the acid from the stalks of a plant she called shamrock – later I learned it was oxalis – and we'd sit, enjoying the stinging taste of the acid; she taught me how to suck honey from the periwinkle flower and to eat and enjoy the sweet floury berries of the hawthorn. She explained that if we were walking to school and separated with a lamp post between us, then we 'had the pip' with each other and were not allowed to speak until we linked little fingers, a gesture that was also necessary when we both said the same word at the same time.

These new rituals delighted me. Poppy taught me how to

'cadge' flowers, too. She explained that any flower which grew through the fence onto the road could be 'cadged' and belong to us, and it wasn't stealing, for they belonged to us *by right*. Each day we'd arrive at school and home with armsful of flowers, the names of all of which Poppy knew and taught me. We were studying grasses and weeds at school, and we were both drunk with the glory of the new names – shepherd's purse, fat hen (what a giggle!), ragwort, where the black and white caterpillars lived, though we preferred the woolly ones that turned into *Red Admirals*.

After school I used to go to Poppy's place to play school in her washhouse, where we lined up her father's empty beer bottles and made them breathe in and out, and do dry land swim with chest elevator, arms bend upward stretch, running on the spot with high knee raising. We also gave them tables and asked them to name and draw the clouds, cirrus, nimbus, stratus, cumulus, while we chanted the names, cirrus, nimbus, stratus, cumulus . . . We made them learn the mountains in the mountain chains, too – Rimutaka, Tararua, Ruahine, Kaimanawa . . . And we strapped them, saying sharply, 'Pay attention. Come out here.' The beer bottles stood in a row on the bench facing northwest, lit golden by the rays of the setting sun shining through the dusty little window. Sometimes, if we broke a bottle, we looked through a piece of glass at the golden world.

* * *

Poppy had two brothers, Bob and Ted, and an elder sister, Florrie, who was soon to be married. Bob, who had left school and was working, was an aloof boy with a black patch over his forehead where he was hurt trying to ride a bicycle down the hospital hill. Rumour said that if he removed his black patch, he would die. His brother, Ted, was short and wide-mouthed like Poppy and of an age for us to tease Myrtle about him. With Florrie's approaching marriage there was much talk among us of weddings and what happened when you married, with our parents giving unsatisfactory answers to our questions.

'What did you do when you married, Mum?'

'Your father and I jumped over a broomstick.'

'And where did the babies come from?'

'From the stork who brings all babies.'

Those answers were as meaningless as the teasing answer people gave when you asked them what they were making: 'A wigwam for a goose's bridle.' Fortunately, Poppy had all the information I wanted.

'You fuck,' she said.

'Fuck?'

'The man gets on top of the woman and puts his thing in her.' She explained to me about fucking and Frenchies, which a man wore on his tool to stop a woman having babies, and how the woman had a cunt and how a man 'came' and shot spunk everywhere, and if the woman started a baby and didn't want it she drank gin to get rid of it. Poppy told me the rhyme:

Pounds shillings and pence
a man fell over the fence.
He fell on a lady
and squashed out a baby.
Pounds shillings and pence.

She knew some Mae West stories, too. Everyone was talking about Mae West and Mae West stories, and at school now, in Silent Reading, we giggled together, changing Whitcombe and Tombs to Tit, come and wombs . . .

Florrie married. We tin-canned her and her new husband and had a feast of fizzy drinks and cakes, and a few days later Myrtle and I and Ted and Poppy went up by the second planny, where the Council men had been cutting down some of the trees, and there, where the trees were lying, among the branches and the pine needles, Myrtle and Ted tried to 'do it' while we watched with interest, seeing Ted jiggling up and down on top of Myrtle.

This new experience pleased me, and anxious as ever to share the day's events, I said casually at the tea table that evening, 'Myrtle and Ted did it in the plannies this afternoon.'

'Did what?' Dad asked.

'Fucked, of course,' I said, quite unaware that I had said anything startling; I was merely recounting the day's events.

There was a sudden sweep of horror that touched everyone at the table, and Dad crashed his fist down, making the tea things (and us) jump. 'I forbid you,' he said, 'ever to speak to Poppy and Ted and any of that family again. As for you,' he faced Myrtle, 'come into the bedroom.'

'Mum,' he called, 'where's the belt.' Mother, who never hit us and was always afraid when Dad asked for the belt, made her plea, 'Don't hit her, Curly.'

The matter was too serious, however. Dad used the belt on Myrtle while I, terrifed, and in a way to 'blame,' fled with the others outside to the summerhouse. I could not understand the sudden transformation of Mum and Dad on receiving my simple item of news. I thought it was an occasion for celebration. I genuinely thought everyone would be pleased.

While Myrtle was crying and screaming in the bedroom, Dad managed to have someone fetch a doctor, for Myrtle, although only twelve now, which was young in those days, already had her 'monthlies,' which Mum had announced by the sewing machine one morning in her disaster voice, saying, 'Myrtle's come, Myrtle's come,' which was confusing until I learned it was not 'spunk' come but 'monthlies.'

The doctor arrived and went to the bedroom to examine Myrtle. We could hear her crying. Dad's fury and fear were unforgettable. The doctor spoke sharply to Dad, saying, 'She's hysterical; she's terrified.'

That night, like the night of Bruddie's illness, effected a change in our lives.

The next morning, when I saw Poppy, I said, 'I'm not allowed to play with you or speak to you ever again.'

She replied, with a tone of equal importance, 'And I'm not allowed to speak to you either.' For Poppy also, unaware of the need for secrecy, had 'told.'

The warning from our parents was so strong, the threat of the consequences of disobedience so dire, that Poppy and I parted forever, and I spoke to her only briefly once, a few years later.

5.

I was born in the South, in an area which at that time was not served with electricity, so that when the sun went down as it early established a habit of doing, slipping beyond the banks of the muddy trout-filled river which belonged to the town and was named after it, or the town was named after the river, and what does it matter, but they lay together on the southern plain, many miles from the sea, and when the sun went down the alarm known as darkness had to be met and provided for by candles and kerosene lamps, held in the hand, preceding you when you walked along dark passages and into dark lonely rooms. My parents controlled the light and walked with it and their bodies were insignificant compared with their giant grotesque shadows striding up the wall and across the ceiling, capturing in their journey the lesser immobile shadows of furniture which nevertheless could change swiftly; everything depended upon the movement of the lamp or candle. The light was not powerful. It did not search into far corners of each room, for the rooms of the house were large and dark with cold floors smelling of pine and a borrowed smell of earth and a dusty spider-webbed smell rising from the foundations beneath the floor. Some parts of the rooms never received the glow of this artificial safeguard against the night. Snap; a shot of electricity, and the guilt is searched out. No, it was not like that. People at night by candlelight and lamplight were immense shadows; it was the shadows which held the power, and everything seemed so strange, out of focus and proportion, with hands creeping along the wall, grasping more shadow, and feet deprived of their purpose, shifting and sliding, 'like tea trays in the sky.'

And all we had was a slight smoky defence against darkness, and in the morning or when we had settled for sleep and the lights were blown or snuffed or pinched out, the only signs of our weapon and the protection it had given us were a few blackened circles burned into the target of the ceiling.

I remember that my mother made this world of shadows

more mysterious by her habit of suddenly putting her head on one side as she walked with the candle or lamp, and saying, 'Hush,' then quoting a snatch of verse or nursery rhyme, in particular the sinister words which set my heart thudding with terror,

> 'Hark hark the dogs do bark,
> The beggars are coming to town.
> Some in rags and some in bags,
> and some in velvet gown.'

And all up and down the gravel roads outside I could hear the barking, and they were no dogs which I knew or had seen by daylight, not collies docilely at heel or briskly setting the sheep in order or bringing home the cows at milking time, but strange menacing dogs, taller than myself, attacking the lonely huddle of beggars who had no house to go to, no bed to sleep in or fire to warm them, but had to pass through a different town each night, secretively, on their lonely journey, trying at all costs to avoid the dogs which lay in wait for them, to tear them to pieces because they did not belong in the town, they were beggars, and some were in rags, and some in bags and velvet gown. Often I heard or seemed to hear an urgent scuffling and wild barking outside our house, then a repeated scraping and knocking, and I would glance at my mother, inquiring, not speaking, Shall I let them in? I hoped that she would say No, never!, for I was afraid of them, and surely our house had no place fit for beggars, surely they were difficult people to fit anywhere, for none of their measurements were like ours! Yet I was disappointed and unhappy when after seeming to listen for a moment to the frantic knocking, my mother yet made no mention of it, as if she had never heard it. Everyone pretended not to hear it. Perhaps it was bad manners to talk of it or seem aware of it. Soon, however, the knocking would cease, there would be a sound of retreating footsteps, and the beggars would be gone on their way, chased by the dogs, to the next house, Mrs Turner's, whose hedge was high and whose lawn was smooth and bright green. And the next morning the streets would be empty of beggars and of giant dogs, with no scrap of rag, bag, or velvet gown lying on the footpath or in the gutter. It was evident that no one in the town had given food or shelter to the beggars, and that even now, in the morning sunshine, they were already on their way, crossing the plains to reach the next town by nightfall. It had not been fair of them or of the dogs to frighten us in the night. I was relieved that they had gone taking their hunger and misery with them.

We had porridge for breakfast, cooked in an iron pot, and stirred with the spurtle which hung on the hook by the stove. We drank big overflowing cups of milk. The sun shone. The lamps and candles were put away. Darkness and the shadows and the beggars would never come again.

On the east coast, in the South, there was a beach, Waipapa, with its own lighthouse. How strange to have a special house for light! But the sea, we learned, could not be relied upon, it was full of whims and treacheries and the bones of dead men, and it was the purpose of the lighthouse to prevent the death of men by warning the ships of dangerous currents or rocks. So many constructions, arrangements, ideas, ways of behaving, were directed to prevent the death of men, of people. People were valuable, though not, of course, if they were beggars, and then the dogs could take care of them in the night. Year after year so many lives were saved by the use of the lighthouse and the powerful beacon restlessly turning and flashing in the dark, controlled and guarded by the Keeper who lived alone in the tower and was supplied with food, fuel, medicine, by a ship whose journey round the coast was often a perilous one: in winter the ship was delayed and for weeks the Keeper received no supplies or letters and talked to no one. His only companion was the light, his only message the distant signals flashed by passing ships; yet locked with his beacon in the stone tower and deprived of most of the amenities of civilization, he remained, they said, one of the happiest men alive. So they said. We played and picnicked in the sand dunes and listened to the seabirds crying, and we stared at the sleeping lighthouse that waited only for the night, to set its beacon revolving and flashing, to save men from death; for during the day the light was no match for the sun, which nevertheless put forth no signals or warnings but allowed men to die; the sun not gesturing with dismay but spreading a silver tinsel on the water as if to say Death is a cheap occasion, a makeshift festival arranged for the benefit of human commerce, with the purchase and exchange of tasteless signed cards of darkness and light and festoons of false glitter tangled between sea and sky. It was terrible that the sun should admit its lack of sympathy with drowning men, should so insistently place the responsibility for pity upon the men themselves – sailing or drowning or walking in smart suits along the streets of the city, or fleeing at night in rags and tags and velvet gown from the savage dogs set upon them by men. The sun rolls over in the sky. The light falls heavily as responsibility. The shoulders of men are bowed under the weight of the light which for all its lack of pity is yet an ally in man's war against death.

And what of the keeper alone for so long with Light?

I was only little, just so high, and I did not consider much about the sun except its burning and sliding down the wet leaves when the rain had stopped, and its quality of morning. I played on the beach among the sand dunes, and listened to the seabirds crying, and then one day I saw a small boat struggling against the waves, being steered from the lighthouse, and as it came nearer I saw that one of the three men in it was waving his arms and screaming while the others tried to cope with him. It was the lighthouse keeper marooned for too long with Light. He had gone mad. The wind was filled with sand, stinging and hot, and the seabirds wheeled and cried. The lonely posturing figure was set down on the beach. He trod the sand as if he believed it might have been water. He tried to reenter the water, to run and plunge in. Then, surrendering because he was being held so tightly by his companions, he stopped the wild moving of his limbs and instead let out a high-pitched scream, like a seabird. He had changed to a seabird.

I did not understand. We were picnicking. We were going to have tomatoes – in sandwiches, and whole with the seeds spitting in our eyes. No one mentioned the lighthouse keeper. My mother turned her face away, as if the beggars had knocked on her door. My father said sharply to me, 'Don't stare at what doesn't concern you!'

So that I missed seeing whether the lighthouse keeper really changed to a bird, flying round and round under the sun, or whether they took him away along the sand to the town where they locked him safely in another tower, as they lock people who have been alone too long with light.

6.

Dear First Dad, Alfred and I and the children, Thomas, Ellen, Milton, have been thinking and talking so much about you lately. The family never tires of asking me about my childhood in Waipori city and Alfred who teaches history at a local college is always pestering me to 'write down' something of my early life and again and again I confront him with – my life has been so happy, where is the history of a happy life? Why wasn't I raped as a child? Why didn't you and mother beat me? Why were not Pearl and I brought up in poverty, forced to walk barefoot through the snow, to witness distressing scenes between parents who never loved each other and took no pains to conceal it, why were we not subjected to subtle cruelties that I could describe in detail? Where are the family skeletons, the uncle who drank and came to our bedroom and got into bed with us, the mad uncle who cut his throat when we were alone in the house, the blood spurting like a fountain over the gold-embroidered cushion on the sofa? Where is the sweet taste of sex that was served to us at the wool store and shearing parties, in the pine plantations, down by the wharves in the dark streets by the grain store and the flour mill? What about the scene in the butter factory or that summer holiday down on the farm when the big hairy rouseabout took me among the milking machines in the cow shed?

* * *

Sometimes in the evening you would sing to me because you liked to sing. The songs were always happy songs. You never sang of the War, you never sang:

I want to go home I want to go home
I don't want to go to the trenches no more
Where the bullets and shrapnel are flying galore.
Take me over the sea
Where the enemy won't get at me.
Oh my I don't want to die
I want to go home.

Oh no, you never sang that song though you had been in the War and when I asked what you had brought back from the war (I being led to believe that the War had been a kind of holiday), you did not show the gas mask and the first-aid kit with the bandages still dark with blood and the paybook with your will written at the end, and the puttees you wound around your legs to keep them dry in the mud of the trenches and the identity disc you wore around your neck; no you brought back none of these from the War. All you had as your souvenir was a clay tablet from Egypt pictured with storks and ibises and beautiful hieroglyphics – some of the first writing, you said, a piece of civilization, to be rescued at all costs from the War; you had brought back a piece of hope, you said, for the future of man. How kind and wise you were! And even when I broke your best, your treasured watch, silver with jewels and a silver compartment you said, 'Naomi dear, what a shame my watch is broken, do not worry, my love for you is worth more than a broken watch.' You never showed anger, desire for revenge. And I remember so well the way you fostered my dramatic talent.

Each year Guy Fawkes was a celebration for you and me and the neighbourhood, culminating in the fireworks and a bonfire

– sparklers, sticks of wire that we held and waved around like a baton while the sparks showered, Catherine wheels pinned to a tree trunk or a plank of wood, spinning in the midst of their flame; ordinary sheets of dark-red crackers strung together by their fuse that could be lit one by one or in a burst of shots from some while others, fizzers we called them, lay hissing, never exploding, while yet others danced as if alive, crackling, leaping until they were exhausted; and then there were the throw-downs, silver three-penny-sized crackers that burst when you threw them on the ground; and skyrockets set in an empty bottle and lit while we watched the slow crawling of the flame along the fuse to the rocket and heard the first hiss as it made ready to fire itself into the air, then whoosh-whoosh there it was away, see where? Where? There. Where? Making a trail of sparks and fire, and we never knew where it really landed, though sometimes the next day or weeks afterwards as we walked the hills or in the streets or even in the garden we might pick up the charred damp remains of a dead skyrocket. And then there was the bonfire, fuelled with old broken-down chairs, tables, manuka scrub, tires – any rubbish that would start the fire that would end by burning Guy that the neighbours' children had trundled through the streets all afternoon crying:

Guy Fawkes Guy
String him on high
A penny for the Guy.

The particular Guy Fawkes Day I write of was when I was fourteen and at high school and in love with a boy who lived on the next street. Though handsomeness at that time was much in demand in boyfriends, with the first question being asked by girlfriends, 'Is he handsome?' meaning does he look like a film star? Donald Parker was not handsome, his cheeks being too ruddy and his eyes too small and his hair too much like straw, but he was clever and I admired his cleverness and his eyes were shy and gentle when he said hello to me. I was hoping he would invite me to the school dance in late November, and this year my invitation to him to attend our Guy Fawkes bonfire was a cunning plan to force a return invitation.

When I told you, dear First Dad, that I had invited Donald you were very understanding, you did not mock me, you were not jealous, oh no, you smiled your approval.

That day stayed for hours and hours in the same place, the middle of a science lesson where I tried to work out chemical formulae and at the same time gaze at the picture on the wall of *The Laughing Cavalier.* I knew the day would sometime start moving again, that it would be precipitated by some force, the nature of which I could not guess but which would not be the mere going down of the sun and the darkening of the world.

I went home from school. I had tea. The world had grown darker. I grew impatient for Donald's arrival. I walked down to the gate and lurked there until I saw him and then I walked casually to meet him.

'Oh, Donald,' I said coldly, with surprise, as if I had met him by chance and was not pleased to see him.

He blushed. I felt triumphant. Then I felt sorry for him with his strawlike hair sticking out at all angles and his face redder than usual, his excitement controlling his body in a way that left his body uncontrolled and his gait awkward. He reminded me of a portrait I had seen of Hans Andersen dancing before the Duchess in Copenhagen, clumsily, believing himself to be performing a ballet as his ambition was to be a dancer; while the duchess and her guests laughed at what they thought were his clowning antics. I remembered how his hair stuck out like Donald's hair, in gold spikes like a drawing of the sun. I remembered how he cried afterwards when he discovered they were laughing at him.

Donald took my hand. His hand felt like rabbit skin when the fur has just been removed: wet and cold. We walked up the path.

'I'm glad you could come to our bonfire,' I said. His awkwardness made my face burn too.

'Dad is so pleased you could come, too. He's arranged a performance in the old summerhouse before we have the bonfire.'

'Oh, you act?'

Donald looked respectfully at me.

'Only with properties Dad has collected. There's a mask he likes to wear, and a few weapons, a rifle, a bayonet, and so on, oh in fun only, and sometimes he likes to dress in soldier's uniform, you'll love my father, Donald, he's kindness itself.'

'He sounds interesting,' Donald said, as we came to the summerhouse where the preliminary drama was to be staged. 'So many parents are out of touch with everything. Just plain dead.'

'You wait till you see my father! Of course my mother died when I was ten years old and I've had the place to myself, being an only child.'

'All my mother thinks of is the Women's Institute, and all my father thinks of is herd-testing and stud bulls.'

'Oh Donald!'

My tone was sympathetic. Donald's father owned the town milk supply and a fine herd of Jersey cattle.

The summerhouse had always been ideal for a theatre. It was covered with banksia roses, tiny yellow roses with buds like dabs of butter, and inside it on this November night there was the smell of the roses, the manuka beams, the damp darkness and the kerosene from the lantern that stood on a small table on the improvised stage.

'Dad is such good fun,' I said, as Donald and I sat on the manuka seats facing the stage.

'What, no audience?' Donald mocked, losing his shyness. 'Am I the only guest?'

'This is a private performance,' I said. 'A family affair. And as the family consists of only my father and myself we are the audience. Later the kids of the neighbourhood will be swarming everywhere for the crackers and the bonfire, not forgetting the fizz.'

'Half of the delight of a play is in the audience,' Donald said in that exasperating way that some of the school girls and boys adopted when they collected new ideas and feelings: a happy confidence of being ahead of the rest of the dumb world and away ahead of the dumb older generation.

Suddenly you, dear First Dad, walked onto the stage.

'That's Dad,' I said, my voice full of pride.

You asked us to come nearer to the stage, and of course we did. I saw that you had put on the gas mask as a Guy Fawkes mask, and it was all I could do to stop myself from bursting into laughter at the comic sight. I'm sure you smiled behind the mask.

'I thought we might act a scene of war this evening,' you said, still smiling.

'Hurrah, hurrah,' I cried, while Donald looked rather puzzled at my enthusiasm.

Then you gave me an old soldier's uniform which I put on, and the mock weapon, the rifle and bayonet, all in fun of course, and then disappearing backstage you appeared with the Guy, such a peculiar Guy with his red face and small eyes painted on and his hair sticking out like wayward straw and his ragged clothes.

'Bayonet practice,' you said, in your military voice.

Naturally I tried to take advantage of my acting lessons although I confess that just a second before I advanced with the bayonet I had a dizzying feeling of strangeness and sickness that vanished almost at once, and then with you, dear First Dad, urging me, dancing up and down in your gas mask with muffled cries of Kill, Kill, Kill I lunged forward with the bayonet and thrust it at the heart of the funny old Guy with his red face, and hair sticking out like yellow straw, the silly old Guy that later we would put on top of the bonfire, in the hot seat, and set fire to in an explosion of fireworks and feasting.

Well, that was that. I doubted if I should ever be called on to play that kind of military role, but you were pleased with my performance although Donald was not, complaining that he had not been able to see the Guy clearly as the kerosene lantern kept flickering and making shadows.

'Don't worry,' you said kindly. 'When the Guy is on the bonfire you will see him clearly, the lighting will be the clearest in the world.'

And you laughed in that kindly reassuring way you had, and our happiness brimming over we all smiled, smiled, smiled.

We made our way to the clearing where the bonfire had been set. You wheeled the barrow with the Guy in it and when we arrived at the place you lifted the sagging form over your shoulders, and, climbing the lower logs of the fire, you set the Guy on top of the pile where it reclined, supported by a chair-shape of logs and old table legs while its straw-colored hair stood in silhouette against the sky. And then suddenly without one firework having been lit, the neighbourhood children arrived and began drinking from the bottles of fizz – raspberry and orange – we had provided for them. As keeper of the Flame in the cement factory you had special skills with Flame and therefore you organized everything perfectly and just as everyone felt that the suspense was too much to bear you lit the first sky rocket, whosh-shsh the signal for the beginning of the festivities. It soared into the sky, surely hitting a few stars before it fell to the other side of the world while the children danced up and down in excitement, begging to have their small slabs of crackers lit, and there was the sour after-smell of gunpowder returning on the wind into our noses and eyes and mouths, and blue misty scribbles of smoke rising in the air, and Catherine wheels, lit, were spinning with blue flame, filled with hundreds of red, blue, green sparks, and with so much banging and crackling and exploding you might have thought a war had started and snipers had begun their fire.

When almost all the fireworks had been set alight, and the time came for the bonfire, there was a sudden hush as effective as if it had been an explosion of sound, and we sat on the grass waiting for the climax of the evening and you, dear First Dad, came up to Donald and asked him, very politely, as he was the guest of the evening, would he have the honour of lighting the bonfire.

'Oh yes please, Mr Livingstone,' Donald said.

He and I walked hand in hand, while the children, seeing us together, began shouting rude rhymes in the way children have.

> The boy stood on the burning deck,
> his feet were full of blisters

he had the pants burned off his bum
so he put on his sister's.

And,

The boy stood on the burning deck
picking his nose like mad
he rolled it into little balls
and threw it at his Dad.

And,

The boy stood on the burning deck
playing a game of cricket
the ball flew up his trouser leg
and hit the middle wicket.

The children shouted and screamed with laughter; they were quite uncontrollable, and if I had not known the words of the sung rhymes from my early childhood I don't think I should have been able to understand them. Nobody seemed to mind the gaiety. We couldn't help being gay when the silly old Guy was about to be burned to death.

A new silence. Donald was the centre of attention. You gave him the matches and you smiled, smiled, smiled while Donald, his face flushed, stooped, struck a match, and put it to the kindling where it flared, spluttered, and died, and instantly there was a sigh of disappointment from the children, and once again Donald stooped and struck a match, and this time it flared into flame that, seizing the fuel in a ragged scissoring clasp and glare, rose, leaping, crackling, hissing where the wood was damp, in the first few moments driving from the wood like the exhalation of breath all the insects who lived there and now scurried to and fro a second before they shrivelled and disappeared; and suddenly in a huge catapulting of flame the Guy was in sight, the poor crazy Guy, the silly old Guy, his straw-coloured hair sticking out like the spokes of the sun, his red-painted cheeks flushed, and as I watched a fantasy came to me that this Guy in his ragged clothes and red face and straw-colored hair was Donald Parker transformed from flesh into rags. The fire roared now to its full height. The Guy was almost burned. Donald and I stood close, watching the body twisting and turning like a live thing in the flames, and it was only my imagination that Donald's face lost its rosy blush and became pale as the face of a dead man, and I did not cling to him, sobbing, digging my fingers fiercely into his wet shirt-covered flesh and there was no startled sigh as if the world had witnessed everything, as if a fire had begun and could not ever be stamped out, oh no, all was gaiety, the children leapt and flew about like birds, the skyrockets soared in showers of multicoloured sparks above the scarred face of the silly old Guy, up and up to the stars, and the moon had risen, and the stars, catching the fever of fire seemed to explode in the moon's face leaving there scarred dark hollows, and the pine trees in the valley grew darker and darker as the last leap of the fire filled the sky, and the only light left in the day settled softly on the leaves of the great pear tree until darkness, heavier than light, plummeted through the air to lie on the earth.

And all was over. The children tasted the last of the gun-powder-raspberry fizz sitting on the rugs and ground-sheets and looking up, up at the Guy whose face only remained a few moments before it was burned. I looked across at you, dear First Dad, and saw that you still wore the gas mask. Then you took it off. Your face was kind, so kind. Then you fired the last rocket. This was the highest rocket of all; no one ever found it.

Donald was far from being a pale trembling schoolboy as he put his arm around me as if I were feeling sad to see the last of Guy Fawkes Day.

'It had to end sometime,' he said.

So the children went home to bed, called by their mothers who *coo-eed* into the night like birds calling from their nests. *Coo-ee, Coo-ee, Coo-ee*, all over the neighbourhood the voices rising and falling.

Donald and I walked to the gate.

'It was a wonderful Guy Fawkes night,' he said. 'Everything

was like a dream. The crackers, the kids, everything. And the silly old Guy burned beautifully.'

Then he kissed me goodbye, seizing me fiercely in a way that robbed me of my breath, and later, when I snuggled into bed, I kept remembering it and how it felt. And that was the end of a very happy Guy Fawkes Night.

Yet I never went to the dance. I knew I had to be loyal to you, dear First Dad, and when Donald Parker hanged himself from a gas bracket in the chemistry laboratory I was shocked, yet I recovered quickly, it was so wonderful to be alive with a father who was kindness itself.

7.

I, self-conscious, restrained, obedient, thinking of myself as responsible and grown up, felt alarm at Isabel's very first move – coming to Training College '*straight from the Fifth Form*' without a year or two years enduring the Sixth Form as a kind of 'discipline for life'. I saw my own world falling apart, all my carefully cemented behaviour crumbling under the force of Isabel's unexpected weather. It was hard work studying both at Training College and University, and with the Social Studies Assignment (the subject already given – 'The Growth Of Cities') supposed to be the length of a book, I could not see how I could 'fit in' Isabel and my apprehension about her survival. My habit of behaving as I was expected to behave – 'obedient, no trouble at all', and my absorption in the world of literature, enabled me to enjoy living a monastic life because no matter how I might desire to be distracted along the way, my pursuit was poetry. My view forward was narrow, and when I glanced aside at others going their different ways, my view remained narrow. I wanted Isabel to be as the dolls had been (clothes-pegs wrapped in cloth) when we pressed them into tiny boxes and kept them there, safely wrapped and snug, able to move only with our help. I wanted her to be a good student, to 'behave', to obey, to study and be approved of by the students and the lecturers, perhaps, though I did not voice this to myself, causing the Principal to say, 'We made no mistake admitting those Frame girls to Training College, they're two of our best students and teachers.' Aunty Isy, expecting another meek Frame who would do her best to be invisible and accept, uncomplaining, the conditions which I myself had set, welcomed Isabel to stay, and when we arrived at Four Garden Terrace and Isabel and I were alone in the small room that we were to share, Isabel was angrily incredulous at the thought of sharing the two-foot-six wide iron bed with me. It had been my fault: I had said timidly, 'Oh that will be quite all right,' when Aunty Isy asked if we could manage.

'But even her thinking of it,' Isabel said angrily.

'Oh don't say anything,' I said, pacifying Isabel. We both knew there was nowhere else to stay at ten shillings a week.

We had little sleep, we were constantly irritated, quarrelling with each other, fighting over our share of the bedclothes, as we used to do at home. Horrified at the uncomplaining way I accepted our tiny ration of food, eating it at the bench in the scullery, Isabel threatened to 'tell Mum' that Aunty Isy was starving us, that she made us eat in the scullery, and sleep in a tiny bed in a tiny room scarcely big enough to swing a cat in, that we were frozen night and day with that cold wind blowing fresh from the harbour or down North-East Valley from Flagstaff and the outlying hills, while Aunty Isy ate in her dining room and toasted her toes in front of a blazing fire.

I persuaded Isabel not to say anything.

'Not just now, wait till the end of term.'

In Isabel's first weeks at Training College she made friends, she found a boyfriend, who became her 'steady' while she was there, although from time to time she had others, and she behaved as I had dreaded she would: she went 'wild' with a wildness that was alarming only to my exaggerated sense of restraint. She discovered roller skating and became an expert skater. She spent every evening at the skating rink while I saw my dream for her future fading and all her 'education' wasted – why did she not study, why did she not seize the opportunity to read, learn? I said little about this to her, for I realized the dreams were mine, and I remembered feeling the same way about Myrtle.

At night, however, when we tugged the bedclothes our way, the extra vicious tug I made towards my side said something of my disappointment in Isabel.

With Isabel at Four Garden Terrace, life had 'episodes'. There was the 'time of the chocolates'. I had peeped, once, into the small front sitting room where the blinds were always drawn and seen propped around the picture rail, an unbroken row of large chocolate boxes decorated with satin ribbon and printed with English and Highland scenes, and winsome photos of animals. When I told Isabel about the chocolate boxes, she said, one day when Aunty Isy was out, 'Let's explore the front room.'

Just inside the door stood a tall chest with drawers full of clothing and photos. In the bottom drawer we found a set of white knitted baby clothes wrapped in tissue paper; there were baby blankets, too, and nappies. We knew that Dad's sisters Polly and Isy had stillborn babies or those who did not survive beyond a few days or weeks, and we'd had a stillborn brother, and even as children we had sensed a kind of hunger in Aunty Polly's and Aunty Isy's feeling towards us, particularly Aunty Isy's interest in Myrtle, and Aunty Polly's voiced desire to 'adopt' Chicks or June. We quickly shut the drawer and turned our attention to the chocolate boxes. We noted that the cellophane seal appeared to be unbroken.

'She can't have kept them all those years,' we said. We knew Aunty Isy had won the chocolates for her Highland Dancing.

'Let's look inside them,' Isabel suggested.

'Oh no, we couldn't.'

'We'll open one and test it.'

As eager as Isabel to explore the chocolate boxes but aware of the responsibilities of an older sister, I was yet happy to use language to conceal the moral problem.

'Yes, let's test them.' After all, testing was different. If the boxes did contain chocolates *testing* would not be *eating*.

We dislodged one box from the picture rail, and carefully untied the ribbon and slipped off the cellophane cover and wedged the upper half from the lower and looked inside at rows of chocolates in their brown pleated cases.

We sat on the sofa and began to taste.

'They're good, not musty at all.'

We continued to eat, and when we had finished the box, we scattered the paper cases inside, shut the box, returned it to its cellophane cover, and retied the satin ribbon in a bow across the front. We climbed up and set the box on the picture rail.

During our stay at Garden Terrace we ate gradually all the chocolates from all the boxes around the picture rail, returning the boxes when we had finished, and each time we sneaked into the darkened front room we remembered the new baby clothes but did not look at them again, and as we ate our fill, we wondered about Aunty Isy and how her life had been and I told Isabel about Uncle George in bed, and the lanoline, and when we scattered the empty paper cases into the empty box we both felt distaste at what we were doing, eating Aunty Isy's cherished souvenirs: eating, eating. The frill around the paper cases was like the frill, withered at the edges, of those small shells you prise open on the beach, to find a small dead heap with a black dead eye lying inside.

It was at the end of the second term that the explosion came. Isabel finally wrote home complaining that Aunty Isy had starved me for a whole year and that we were both starving and during that winter we were freezing in one bed in a tiny room. Isabel's letter prompted a swift reply from mother to Aunty Isy who then wrote to Dad, her brother, expressing the opinion that 'Lottie has always been a bad manager.' Mother's indignant reply was followed by Aunty Isy's accusation that she had been mistaken in thinking Isabel and I were 'lovely girls'. We had eaten all her souvenir chocolates! Apparently on a rare visit to the front room she found a stray chocolate case on the carpet.

In the exchange of letters, Uncle George's sisters found disparaging things to say about the 'awful Frames', how the children had always been out of control, running wild on the Oamaru hills, how the Frame home was like a pigsty, mother didn't know the first thing about housekeeping. The bitter correspondence continued between Dad and Aunty Isy (mother refused to lower herself by writing after her first two letters), with Dad now using Mum's formal name, Lottie.

The result was that Isabel and I moved from Number Four Garden Terrace, I with shame and embarrassment and a sense of loss in being no longer thought of as a 'lovely girl, no trouble at all', and Isabel with triumph because we had asserted our 'rights'. Isabel happily, sociably going to live among friends in a boardinghouse whose landlady was well known and liked by a succession of students, I to the only other place available, Stuart House, a hostel where I rented a 'cubicle' for the rest of the year – a narrow space in a large room where each bed was screened by a fibreboard wall about six feet high; and I found little solitude or privacy for studying, reading and writing – and sleeping.

I knew during the first weeks of Isabel's stay in Dunedin that she was lost from me, and I felt sad to lose her: after all, she had been Emily,

> No coward soul is mine,
> No trembler in the world's storm-troubled sphere.

I think her separation from me was accomplished in those evenings when she skated spinning round and round the rink almost as if unwinding an anchoring thread from her body. She spent hours swimming, coming home to Garden Terrace with her blonde hair green-tinged from the chlorine in the water, and when she opened the door of our room I would always see, behind the face of the student who had been swimming, the face of the child coming home from the baths the day Myrtle was drowned.

The shift from Garden Terrace almost completed our separation. If we saw each other at Training College we said hello in an embarrassed way. And when the letter came from home we met each other briefly to talk about the awful news: 56 Eden Street which we'd rented all those years of our growing up had been sold and the new owner, soon to be married, had given us notice to move out at the end of the year.

Shortly after that the warden of the College sent for me, and when I wonderingly arrived for the interview, she began, 'I want to talk to you about your sister Isabel.'

Isabel, she said, was making a guy of herself both by her behaviour and by the clothes she wore, in particular a skirt printed with a giraffe.

'Fancy wearing a skirt with a giraffe printed on it!' the warden said.

I murmured something sympathetic towards Isabel. Her clothes never shocked us; they were interesting, original. Knowing how many hours we Frame girls had spent trying to sew our own clothes, fitting petersham, making hems even, matching that awkward scoop at the arm of a sleeve to ensure the right sleeve was in the right arm, I thought Isabel's appliquéd giraffe was a triumph of dressmaking. The truth was that no one else had a skirt with a giraffe on it, therefore Isabel was condemned for her difference. The force of 'no one else' was a familiar feature of our lives.

'You as her elder sister, are responsible for her,' the warden said. 'Try to influence her not to be so . . . so . . . outlandish.'

I, demure in my ordinary print dress and cardigan, said, as one grownup to another, 'She's very young,' adding, as if I knew the reason for Isabel's behaviour (why should not Isabel have suffered the misery of being in the Sixth Form?), 'she came to Training College too early.'

Then, alarmed, indignant, unhappy, I murmured something about 'conditions at home'. There was sickness, I said, bursting into tears. 'And we're being turned out of our house and we have to find somewhere before Christmas.'

'Well,' the warden said, 'see what you can do to influence your younger sister.'

I said nothing to Isabel about my interview with the warden. I was angry with the concern over a mere giraffe, and now, so many years later, the episode seems unbelievable and wryly amusing but it does show the degree of conformity expected of us. I was ashamed, too, of bursting into tears, although later I hoped the episode had enhanced my poetic role – 'illness in her family – perhaps drink? – turned out of her home . . . a fitting source for a poet . . . what a tragic life . . .'

A few weeks later the warden again 'sent for' me, this time to congratulate me on the children's story I had written and to ask me if I had thought of 'taking up' writing for children. My work showed promise and imagination, she said, while I listened calmly, inwardly disdainful of devoting my life to anything but writing poetry, cherishing the idea of myself as a poet. At the end of the interview the warden said, 'Our little talk seems to have had an effect on your sister; she's much more subdued now and no longer wears that skirt with the giraffe on it.' I didn't explain that the giraffe had become dislodged and Isabel was hoping to sew it when she had 'time'.

8.

January 20th

It is almost the end of the first month of a new year. I feel I have done nothing, though what I should be doing I do not know, it is just the feeling of getting nowhere and of time passing. I shall be twenty-eight this year, nearly thirty, then forty, and then come the fifties and sixties, why in no time I shall be an old woman collecting an old age pension. I am afraid to think of it. Why, it will happen in almost no time. My own mother is old and ill, they say she will die soon with her heart. I shall get old like her and have high blood pressure and varicose veins and dropsy and have to squeeze the salt out of every pound of butter and remember not to put salt in the vegetables or on lettuce or any food because it is forbidden. Or perhaps I shall get diabetes like my grandmother, and not eat sugar, and have my legs taken off, to be kept behind the door in the dark.

Enough of this morbid writing. It just happens that I seem

to be doing the same thing over and over every day – get up, get dressed, get the breakfast, dress the children, Peter and Mark, or pester them till they dress themselves, send them out to play, give baby her bottle and put her down to sleep, have a peaceful cup of tea – that means a cup of tea in peace – with Tim before he goes off to work, wash the dishes, vacuum the carpets, turn on the washing-machine, wash, rinse, spin-dry, hang out the washing, sit down to morning tea with the paper to read and the scandal.

And so on and on. In the afternoon I have time to read. I am reading *The Tenant of Wildfell Hall* by Anne Brontë. It is the story of a woman and her drunkard husband, her suffering and terror in a world of squalor – that is what it says on the cover. I find the book absorbing, indeed I dare not put it down. What will Huntingdon do next, I ask myself, quivering, like his wife Helen, for fear and suspense. What a brute of a man to so treat a woman's love. The scene where Huntingdon has a rendezvous in the shrubbery with his current mistress, and his wife, taking a solitary walk in the same area at nightfall, is mistaken by Huntingdon for the woman he has promised to meet, and therefore greeted passionately and fondled, until he discovers his error and exclaims in disgust and fear, – My wife! Helen! – that scene abhors and disgusts me. I have read it carefully three times.

Sometimes in the afternoon I have visitors like the Baldwins, Benny and Ted, or the Smarts, Terry and Josie. Very often Benny and Josie call and we sit and talk babies and husbands and housework over a cup of tea and biscuits. I feel so ashamed that I never have tins full of my own cooking when visitors call – I have to undo the cellophane off packets of biscuits, chocolate and wafers, and pastries; and though Benny and Josie are too polite to make remarks, I feel their criticism, for they always have meringues or peanut brownies or those pinky marshmallow cakes, when I visit them. Benny's father is a judge in the Supreme Court and her husband is high-up in the Civil Service. The Smarts have a new house over in one of the bays – a coming area, they say. They know the Bessicks, Dr Herbert and his wife Alison, and have promised us an introduction. Dr Bessick is a brilliant gynaecologist, just returned from studying overseas – his wife had an article in the social news about their life on the continent and the States. She is a bit of a shrew, they say, but dresses perfectly and is, they say, an entertaining hostess. Both the Baldwins and the Smarts, by the way, are in the local drama club. We have playreadings on Tuesdays.

Now how else shall I describe my day? In the evening after tea there is always the children's bath and story, for Tim and I believe in the idea of putting children to bed after a story. Tim bought a book on child psychology, and we have studied it. Some of the ideas do not seem to work with Mark, he is so individual and temperamental. Tim reads the story while I fix the baby's bottle. Children's books are different now from when I was a child. I have enjoyed reading *Jemima Puddleduck*, by Beatrix Potter, I had never read it before, how the foxy gentleman kept his newspaper in his tail coat pocket and had a shed full of feathers for Jemima Puddleduck to lay her eggs in. What a cunning swindler was the foxy gentleman, and how gullible poor Jemima Puddleduck. It was almost like real life with its intrigue and near-murder.

By the way, Tim has bought me an electric cake mixer so that I can make a chocolate and walnut sponge for the weekend when we meet the Bessicks. It'll be strange to meet a doctor socially, especially a gynaecologist, though I shall be too seasoned to blush if I remember what he must know about the insides of women. Ten years ago I should have fled. Just imagine.

It is late now and I am tired. Tim has just gone down to the gate with the milk bottles. Oh, the weather is so hot and humid, I don't know how I can bear it sometimes. And the mosquitoes, there seems to be a plague of them this year – they say there have never been so many. I shall go to bed soon. Benny says she uses Wisteria Night Cream, that it is better than Gloria Haven. I have tried Gloria Haven before and I, too, feel there is something lacking in it. Today I bought a pot of Wisteria at the chemist's, extravagance no doubt, but Tim does not mind, indeed he encourages me, and likes to see me taking an interest in my make-up. What a perfect husband. Where in all the world would I find a man more thoughtful or loving? And to think that years ago he was one of those dirty little boys who used to hang around my sister Francie at Waimaru, and I used to poke my tongue out at him. His father was a council man, and though Tim began his first year medical, he did not finish it, it was not suited to his talents. He is now high-up in selling, not a mere commercial traveller, but a high pressure executive with responsibility. His friend Howard Weston (the Westons have a sheep station in the country back of Waimaru) has fixed the sale of our new house at Waimaru. When I saw the pictures and plans of it, I thought it seemed strange that it should be built over the old rubbish dump where we used to play as children and where Francie was burned. The idea frightened me. Living where we used to sit amongst the toi-toi, tickling it down our backs and putting it in our hair for feathers; where we explored and found what we called treasure, old tyres and boots that we said were walked in at night by dead men and giants; and bits of motor cars, and books, and all the rubbish under the sun. And from morning to night, how long seemed the time, with the day taking chicken steps in the sky. Yes, when I live in our house there I shall feel afraid and strange; yet I feel it is the right place to live; the place with its promise of happiness and treasure in our future life and then its despair over Francie, I had a blue ribbon in my hair that day, and it kept coming undone and there was no one to tie it for me; it is like a kind of gap in my life. What nonsense I talk.

Now I must stop writing in this diary for tonight. Tim is in the bath. He always runs it far too hot so that the place is all steam and his body like a cooked crayfish; and he even *reads* in the bath. Dear Tim! To think I have been married eight years. Now I must go to bed, and before I sleep, finish one more chapter of *The Tenant of Wildfell Hall.*

January 21st

I am excited over meeting the Bessicks. And afraid. It will be my first *real* experience of hostessing to people who really matter. I have asked them to come in the evening for I think it would be more convenient and less nerve-racking with the children asleep, though I had wanted to show off Sharon's curly hair and dimples and that charming smile of hers, and the pink nylon frock, embroidered in Switzerland. Never mind. To fill in a little of the evening, if conversation lags, we have arranged to play Beethoven's Fifth Symphony on the radiogram. I am quite safe with that for I have read about it and what it is meant to represent and know the different movements, and therefore should be able to make some intelligent remark about it. I believe the Bessicks are musical, and I feel quite safe with the Fifth Symphony. I can mention about fate knocking on the door and that kind of thing. I shall do out the sitting-room in the afternoon so as to have it ready, and make the sponge in the morning. I have decided on coffee sponge instead of chocolate as coffee is more intellectual. I shall wear a simple tasteful frock of taffeta, with my new gipsy earrings, and my hair done as usual with the parting slightly higher. It ought to settle if I wash it the night before, Friday night, or perhaps two nights before, Thursday, and then it will be manageable.

You must forgive me for writing all this, but it absorbs me, you know. They say Herbert Bessick is unique.

January 22nd

Hot weather still. The children are running around bare. I had a letter from Daphne today, the first for a long time. What a strange world she must be living in! Her letter does not make sense, it is a wonder the doctor let it be posted – all about Christmas and a piece of moon and a mouse nibbling at a shroud of sun, it frightens me, I can never see her getting better and living a normal life like myself. Poor Daphne. And she sends back the letter I wrote her, and has written the words Help help help at the end of my letter. As if I had to be rescued from a terrible doom, as if fate (I think of the Fifth Symphony) knocked at my door. Poor Daphne. Naturally she means herself when she cries help help help.

* * *

January 24th

I had a strange dream last night. I dreamt I was sitting in the middle of the arena at a circus, nursing a little black panther that kept scratching at me and saying in a child's voice with a foreign accent – I'll scratch your eyes out. I'll scratch your eyes out.

The spotlights of the circus played over me, and though I knew I was expected to perform in some way, I found that I could not remember my act. The audience in the big top cheered and stamped and whistled, waiting for me to begin. Suddenly I threw the panther away from me across the ring and began to cry, and I thought, This is only a dream, there is nothing to cry about, it is just a dream. Then the light in the circus faded and I found myself in Paris, walking by the Seine river. It was midnight. I heard a clock striking twelve, and I kept on walking looking down at my shadow cast in the water to make sure it was walking with me. Suddenly I felt tired and knew I must sleep, so I took off my black fur coat – thinking, how strange, I did not notice I wore a black fur coat – and spread it on the ground and fell asleep on it. When I awoke my fur coat had vanished, my shadow had vanished, I was standing staring in the river that swirled in a whirlpool of darkness.

Now isn't that a weird dream? I asked Tim if he dreamt a dream last night, and he said no, except at one time he half dreamt he was climbing a mountain to find an orchid, but found only a handful of snow. Dreams are curious things. They say that dreams mean more than people think.

By the way, when I first began this diary I said I would give a record of my inner life. I begin to wonder if I have said anything about my inner life. What if I have *no inner life?* I am morbid today. I had a letter from my mother in Waimaru. She says the same thing over and over in her letters; that everything is well, that everybody is happy; and she says it like a chant of denial, so that you can't help knowing that nothing is well, and nobody is happy. Sometimes I wonder if we should go south to live. I don't know. I really don't know.

Today and tomorrow and then the day of my little social gathering. I am beginning to wonder if I should make a coffee sponge after all, for we shall be having coffee to drink, and it may seem like too much of the same thing. I shall forget about it, let the idea stay in my unconscious mind, and decide tomorrow whether it shall be chocolate or coffee. If it were chocolate I could use real chocolate, plain or dark, melted, or cocoa. Tim has said something about drinks, a liqueur, benedictine, or tia maria, but I am not sure how to time drinks and I don't want to disgrace myself by showing ignorance.

I don't know if I have told you that Terry and Josie cannot come on Saturday because of their children's chicken-pox. We shall have to entertain the Bessicks alone. What a frightening prospect. I am relying on Beethoven's Fifth Symphony to break the ice.

January 25th

I am afraid for tomorrow night.

Sunday

Well, it is over now and I can look at it calmly and with indifference. Shall I describe last night? Well, before they came I had the children put to bed and the baby given her bottle, and the sitting room arranged cosily and, I hope, tastefully, with the chairs and couches (our furniture is Swedish make) placed at what Tim and I consider the correct angle so as to make conversation easier and more intimate. I dusted the radiogram and blew the fluff from the long-playing needle, and left the Fifth Symphony lying upon the cabinet. I could not help leaving a few of our more intellectual books lying around, carelessly, as if we used them every day, some of them half-open, or open at pages of difficult words; also a collection of Van Gogh prints, and an isolated Picasso, which I propped up on the top shelf of the bookcase. It was one of Picasso's that I cannot make head or tail of, yet it gives a certain impression and surely no visitor, I thought, would be boorish enough to ask me to explain the meaning of it.

Tim had decided that we wouldn't have any drinks, only coffee, and that the cake had better be chocolate, with walnuts, for variety. I prepared to make a number of narrow slices of toast with a sardine, or a slice of tomato, lying upon each. Above all I wanted our evening to be a *natural* one, with none of the artificialities one finds – everyone at ease and happy.

They came at eight o'clock. I was aflutter when I heard their car – one of the latest, with engine in the back. I dashed to the bathroom for a final powdering and a new touch of lipstick and whipped open the cupboard door to make sure the plates and coffee cups were ready, and as a last minute thought, I put the Picasso, face downward, upon the card table. I was afraid suddenly that Dr Herbert would say, outright – What is your interpretation of this picture, Mrs Harlow? (Later, I thought, when we become friends, we shall of course be Tim and Teresa and Herbert and Alison.) Then I answered the knock at the door, quite coolly, though my voice shook, and I was forced to clear my throat.

They are such nice people. We were Tim and Teresa and Herbert and Alison right from the very first, though I do not remember actually addressing the doctor by his christian name in case it sounded familiar, though he has travelled overseas and does not worry about such things. He called me Teresa. His voice is very soft, almost like fur, and he is dark, slightly bald, with brown eyes, almost black at times; and his wife is the opposite, very thin, with fair hair and large grey eyes, nondescript except for their size. She has a protruding upper lip, something to do with her teeth, which gives her a horsey expression. Admittedly she is good-looking in other ways, her eyes for example, but I can see what Josie means when she describes her as a shrew. The expression is latent. She kept referring to her husband as *Doctor.* I could see she is conceited about being a doctor's wife. Yet I enjoyed the evening. We played the Fifth Symphony, and Herbert said, instantly – Fate knocks on the door.

And he (Herbert I mean, not Fate) gave me quite a special sort of smile. Herbert (forgive me if it sounds familiar) tapped with his hand upon the side of the chair and nodded his head to the music, with an understanding look in his eye, while his wife sat with a slight smile on her face and her eyes in a kind of dream which I must confess made them rather ethereal. I had prepared to nod my head and tap too, to show my familiarity with the piece, but I had to devise some other means of keeping time. I swayed backward and forward with, I hope, an intelligent expression on my face. Tim said afterwards that I looked like a charmed snake. Dear Tim, what a tease he is!

After the music Dr Bessick (I have decided that the name Herbert sounds too familiar) exclaimed that the Fifth Symphony was one of his first loves, and repeated the words – Fate knocks at the door, again glancing at me with a special look in his eye.

He said something in French then, which, although I thought rapidly to connect with any sentences of French words I knew, I could not understand, and answered – Yes, yes, rather foolishly, but with French gestures, for compensation. I did hope then to make a remark in French to show him that I knew a little of the language, but alas all I could think of was – *Le chat court vite. Le rat court vite aussi.*

Oh, we had the usual annoying things happen in the evening. The sardines came out squashed, and I burned a couple of slices of toast. They complimented me on the coffee. They said – Do you grind your own coffee?

I was about to say, of course not, when I realized that it is apparently the thing to grind your own coffee, so I said – I have been thinking of doing so.

Oh, you find the bought coffee ghastly too, questioned Mrs Bessick.

I told her I found the bought coffee hopeless, but managed to process it in some way.

Oh, we talked then about capital punishment and the Far East, and the psychology of the child, and Alison told me of her child, Magdalen, very highly strung and delicate and brilliant – Poor little Magdalen, I said. She will suffer.

And Alison said – It's terrible. We don't know what kind of world our children will grow up into. If only something could be done about the state of the world.

We were both silent then, and depressed. I agreed – If only something could be done about the state of the world.

The Bessicks have promised to come again, or ring us quite soon. I believe now, fingers crossed, that we are established in the right society.

Thursday, February the something

Everything is flat. The Bessicks have not rung, and thinking it over, I believe they never will. The weather continues hot and at night the air breathes mosquitoes. I cannot remember a summer for so long without rain. The ground is like a baked brick, cracked and hard, and the children dance over the cracks and call them earthquakes. Of late in the afternoon I have been taking a rug on the lawn and lying down in my sunsuit, lazily drowsing or looking up at the sky where you can see the waves of heat moving and shimmering. I remember when we were children we used to lie for hours looking up at the sky in autumn when the thistledown sailed above the cloud, sailed or scurried on an urgent voyaging. Where? And then a cloud would cross the sun and we would shiver for the blocked warmth, and it would seem as if there had never been any sun, as if we had lived always in cold; until the cloud passed and we shivered for the warmth of new sun upon our backs, between the shoulder-blades where cold and hot strike. It's funny, the sky up in the north here is different from the sky in the south, and the light too. Down in the south you feel all the time a kind of formidable background, like a block of grey shadow, of a continent of ice, Antarctica in the wings. The dark there is more frightening and less friendly, you are trapped in it as in a tomb, and the stone of ice will not roll away. Up here at night there is a kind of upper daylight, high in the sky, as if the dark were clinging closer to the earth under the whip and strike of sun. But, why, how strangely I express myself. I was thinking of the letter Daphne wrote to me, about dark and light and a continent of ice. I must send her a tin of biscuits.

By the way I had a letter from my mother to say that Toby is coming north for a night and expects to stay with me. I don't want him to come. He lazes around and expects to have everything done for him, and he won't eat this and he won't eat that, like a spoilt child, the way he acts at home. And I'm afraid he would disgrace me and take a fit when I had visitors. I shall live in terror that some of my friends will call and see Toby hanging around with his dirty fingernails and greasy hair. Perhaps I should be sorry for him. But his life is so apart from mine, him poking about in these rubbish dumps for scrap iron and bottles and things to sell, almost as if he were still a child. He goes back and back to the rubbish dumps as a child goes to a wound, tearing the plaster off so that it never heals but festers always. I do not know why I thought of that. I just thought of it.

February 11th. Monday

The Bessicks have still not rung, as they promised. Rain today and I could have put my tongue out and drunk it straight from the sky. It was the kind of rain that smokes with warmth. If I were in the south now there would be signs of autumn, leaves turning, and the chill in the later afternoon, and the beginning of mushrooms in the sheltered and more dewy places. Here there seems nothing but warmth and everlasting summer. I had another letter from Daphne, a very strange letter. I don't know if they will ever cure her, even with these modern treatments like electric shock and insulin shock and that new kind of brain operation you read about in the papers, the kind where they change the personality. How terrible to be deprived of one's personality.

February 18th. Monday

Alison Bessick has been shot through the left lung and they have arrested her husband for murder. Isn't it awful? I can scarcely believe it. In spite of the fact that it is in this morning's paper, on the middle page, with a photo of their house and the room where the murder was committed. I can scarcely believe it. Isn't it awful, really awful?

February 19th. Tuesday

The place is agog with the Bessick murder. There are all kinds of rumours. Some say she was carrying on with a man from one of the East Coast bays, some say *he* was carrying on with one of his women patients, and that Alison found out and confronted him and he shot her, in cold blood. Some say he went berserk and that his counsel will put in a plea for not guilty on the grounds of insanity. Others say his wife had it coming to her. You've no idea, there are so many rumours. Our home was one of the last they visited together. To think of it. I see now when I look back on our evening that things were not as they should have been between them. He seemed to have a calculating coldness in his manner. I realize the significance of it now.

MARRIED TO A MONSTER. That's the title of one of the films in town this week, and I do believe it applies to some homes where women are forced to suffer cruelty and coldness from their husbands. I thank heaven that Tim is beyond reproach.

■ 9.

The fernhouse of the Gardens had been built many years ago, and stood to the left of one of the two main gates, in the deep shade of a row of umbrella trees. Though the walls and roof were of glass, they had long ceased to look like glass, for the atmosphere within exuded a green and yellow damp slime that clung to the walls and the ceiling, clouding the glass, making the darkened daylight within seem more dark and mysterious. The fernhouse was like a miniature artificial bush. Ferns overhung or sprouted in tubs; a noise of gushing creeks came from the one hose that sprouted water onto the ferns and shrubs and into a moss-lined pond. Never had there seemed to be so much water to spare; as if the genuine bush, learning of this artificial corner of itself in the Matuatangi Gardens, had sent part of itself there to strengthen the illusion of real bush. Unlike the human body that rejects an alien likeness, the bush, with ambassadorial welcoming had adopted, had grafted the fernhouse to itself.

Walking on the grass in the Gardens, Malfred and Wilfred had felt the dampness on their shoes and their feet. The grass was softly springing with rain, like moss. Yet, inside the fernhouse where there had been no rain, they found that their feet and legs were instantly soaking, and as they walked past the rows of ferns that drooped as if from a recent downpour, the fronds brushed a saturation of drops onto their coats and faces and hair.

It had been raining when they walked there for the last time together. Once inside the fernhouse they found again this phenomenon of an oozing, moss-lined, mysteriously rain-fed world. Malfred, turning to Wilfred, saw him in this dim, green bush-darkness. He saw reflected in her hair the green plait of pond slime that trailed across the ceiling of the house and down the walls onto the cold concrete floor. Smelling the moss was like breathing in soft, fine rain that had lain in the earth, had evaporated, then had fallen, exuding its own memorial, into their throats. Malfred shivered. The creeks, flowing from nowhere, trickled, gushed, bubbled. Some of the ferns were yellowing at the edges, dying in spite of the excess of moisture.

'Let's go out of here,' Malfred said. Her voice was breathless.

Wilfred spoke slowly, stolidly almost. 'Why?'

'Well, it's cold and damp. The sun never comes here. I don't know why *we* came here; with so much to do, and plan, and there's the Art Society Dinner, and this whole side of the Gardens is in shade all day. Look at that cracked window!'

Wilfred did not say, 'To hell with the Art Society Dinner.' He took Malfred in his arms and kissed her, and she stood, surprised, warm, not knowing what to do.

'Give me your tongue,' he said.

She felt alarm, then warmth again, and a taste of moss, like the green tongues of moss curled on the windows and the ceiling. And then, when Wilfred put his hand inside her dress she felt a damp steam, like sweating fern, rise from between her breasts. And then she jerked her head back and began to cry, and it seemed that all her gentleness flowed away with her tears, for she felt callous, aged, experienced and she did not care when Wilfred, a deep flush spreading under his skin, said, 'Excuse me,' and went behind the wet, black-barked treefern, and she thought as they linked arms, easily now, and walked out of the fernhouse that the white specks and spatters on the fern looked like a new kind of mildew, a disease that the ferns had caught through being there, in the fernhouse, at that moment.

A month later Wilfred sailed with the troops, and she never saw him again. Nor did she ever go again to the fernhouse, though before she left Matuatangi forever she walked one afternoon through the Gardens and spent a half hour sitting in the sun on the stone seat of the Chinese Gardens that had been planted a year ago, with much ceremony, with dancing in the streets (dancing in the streets in Matuatangi!) and a Chinese feast put on by the Chinese community. The new Gardens replaced the old fernhouse which had been pulled down. These were dry, brilliant, formal gardens with miniature trees, a gold fish pond, an arranged stream (not creek) flowing decorously from a visible concrete channel. There were no ferns, no moss, and no shade, for the row of umbrella trees had been cut down. The fernhouse was gone forever.

10.

It seemed now so long ago – it was more than six years – since I had first been in Ward Four and gone out walking and stared curiously and sadly at the crazy people of Ward Two, noting their weird hats, crumpled coats, twisted stockings; and their childish excitement at whatever lay around them; how they pointed ecstatically to the ordinary everyday sun standing habitually in the sky and the flowers that startle with their silence even more than their colour, growing along the garden borders; how they stood, dazzled, at the sign of a figure in shirt sleeves who seemed to them to be the doctor, mowing his front lawn while his wife sat near, dandling their white-haired child.

Now that I belonged to Ward Two I also gaped amazedly at the spectacle of the powerful sun policing the earth, Move On There No Loitering, while the arrested darkness lay dungeoned, awaiting trial. The sun seemed closer, more threatening, with warrants of execution slipped between the shafts of light and placed strategically, like shadows, so that we could read them and take warning, perhaps adopt emergency measures. When I walked with Ward Two it was not the Ward Four sun that stood in the sky, nor the Ward Four flowers that puppeted brightly in the light wind. We saw the sinister collisions of colour and heard the explosions along the garden border. We looked with gratitude on the poplar trees and the fear that predisposed them to sudden shiverings reached us through secret channels, causing us to shiver as well. On every occasion I seized the opportunity to walk in the grounds, but Sister Bridge, knowing that I liked to be out under the sky, gave orders that I was not to be 'indulged.' 'Someone who deserves the outing can go,' was her verdict. 'Someone who knows how to behave herself instead of running screaming from the meal tables and crying if I put her in the dirty dayroom as if she were better than the others when in fact she's worse.'

Yet it was the policy of Sister Bridge to encourage everybody from the clean dayroom, and those who could be allowed for a short time from the dirty dayroom, to take part in all official outings – walks, church, dances. Cliffhaven was progressing in its adoption of the 'new attitude.' In the coat cupboard there hung a collection of ward dresses, pastel-shaded party dresses in stiff shiny materials with gathers pleats and flares and sometimes matching underskirts in parchment nylon, all bought with hospital funds by the Matron on a special expedition to town, and issued for 'outings' to those with nothing else to wear, which meant those without visitors. Although Matron Glass was constantly telling me to 'write to your people and tell them you need clothes,' I did not do so, for my parents either had no money or did not realize that mental patients wear clothes other than the pants which arrived for me in festive parcels at Christmas time and on birthdays.

I was grouped, therefore, with the 'forgotten' and with those, also usually 'forgotten,' who would be in hospital until they died. This grouping had its pleasures. One day we were fitted for new skirts and sweater sets, and their arrival was an exciting event, if one did not think too much about the fact that one had been chosen to wear what could be called the uniform of the dead. I still could not believe there was no hope for me, or I kept running over the rat-infested no man's land between belief and disbelief and pitching camp on one side or the other. I dithered in Time, not knowing what to call forth from the future, fearing to face the present and the cruelty of Sister Bridge and the penances she imposed upon me, and not daring to turn to the past. So I was silent, attacking my time-bordered self, blighting, like black frost, the edges of my life until they crumpled and dropped in the bitter southeast wind from the sea.

Yes, we danced, the crazy people from Ward Two whom even the people from the observation ward and the convalescent ward looked upon as oddities and loonies. We dressed in our exotic party dresses, taffetas and rayons and silk jersey florals, and we lined up outside the clinic to have make-up put on our faces from the ward box with its stump of lipstick, coated and roughened powder puffs, box of blossom-pink powder and scent bottle squirting carnation scent behind our ears (who did we expect to kiss them) and in the hollow of our wrists. By the time we were ready we were a garden of carnations and we looked like stage whores.

There was excitement, a sweating pleasantness and promise which made our noses shine in spite of the slapped-on powder puff, and slowly dampened and stained the underarms of our dresses. Matron would arrive, breathless and pink cheeked and tell us, like a messenger bearing news from a far country, that 'Ward Four were ready ages ago and have gone through to the hall' or 'Ward One are just going through' or 'The band has arrived.' This would only increase the excitement and those who simmered over beyond control would have to be skimmed away to bed, and others reduced by cold threats to a reasonable calm. Matron Glass would smile, and Sister Bridge would smile and compliment us on our appearance and warn Carol about getting with her partner into dark corners of the men's dining room where we were to have our supper, and it would at last be time to go across the dark yard that was wet with dewfall, through Ward One with its smell of wet cots and scabbed skin and the personal smell, the passport or free sample that death provides for old women, along the visitors' corridor with its prison atmosphere, barred fire, brown polished linoleum and long leather seats with upright backs, through to the unfamiliar part of the hospital, to the dreariness and barrenness that are peculiar to the men's wards; and at last to the Big Hall with its bright lights and powdered floor, and along the walls the seats half-filled on one side with men and on the other side with women, and down at the back, facing the stage, the red plush armchairs for the officials – the doctors and perhaps visitors invited from town to see mental patients engaged in recreation. The officials usually arrived a short while before supper, and the doctor present would be the one on duty.

The band sat on the stage, making lightheaded preliminary music. We found places against the wall. The lights dazzled. 'Istina, Edith will look after you,' Edith would say, half-pulling me to a seat. 'You sit beside Edith.' When the last group from the male side had arrived, looking self-conscious with slicked-down hair and pressed trousers and white handkerchiefs peeping from pockets, and when the last group of women entered – the blasé convalescents from the Cottage, exclaiming petulantly that they didn't really want to go dancing but their ward sister had made them and anyway they thought they'd see what all the fuss was about, then it was time to begin.

I couldn't help staring at the Ward Four people who looked opulent in their own clothes. Mrs Pilling wearing jewelry and Mabel in the glistening moth-eaten evening dress which she always wore as the partner of Dick the patient in white tie and tails and white gloves.

The band started a waltz.

'Nice and old-fashioned,' a nurse said. 'Get up and dance, everyone.'

The men either stood rigidly against the wall or rushed helter-skelter across the room to clasp a partner and whirl her away to dance with or without her consent. Sometimes one of the men, having chosen his partner and danced a few steps with her, decided she did not suit him after all, and he would walk away and partner someone else; sometimes a woman ran across the room to choose her man. There were few ballroom formalities and much of the 'plain-speaking' that makes a virtue of insult; there were endearments and pledges and muddled conversations following the first remark which was not, 'A good floor isn't it?' but 'How long have you been here?'

Most of the patients who had been in hospital a long time had their faithful partner. Mine was Eric, a middle-aged balding man who reminded me strangely of a conjurer who used to visit us at school at the end of the term and charged us threepence to see him spread satin cloths over the classroom table and draw silk handkerchiefs from a top hat, and who, although he never performed a complicated miracle like cutting people in half or climbing a rope to the ceiling of the classroom, could always be relied upon to make no mistakes with the satin cloth and the silk handkerchiefs.

Eric was unromantic, but he kept in time with the music and he did not tread on my feet. His mouth hung open, his head was thrust forward and his brow glistened with the oil of endeavour and concentration. I waited patiently for him to perform a miracle just as I had waited for the school conjurer after I had staked my threepence; nothing but satin cloths and silk handkerchiefs; the face of the world stayed the same, the sick were not healed, the roof did not dissolve and let in the stars.

Eric taught me to dance. We danced the Destiny,

My dear I love you so
Just pack up your trousseau . . .

He was pedantic and fatherly and usually took me to supper and we ate steadily, like reading a book and not missing a single word, through the sandwiches to the scrumptious cakes with fancy icing until the drinks arrived, bloating and vivid and fizzy, one bottle each, or two if you were cunning or had an enterprising partner. All romance was abandoned for the feed. I remember one partner who did not open his mouth except to eat and to say to me, before passing from the sandwiches to the cakes, 'After this I'll feel your leg.'

Our hearts beat fast with sheer greed at the sight of the food; there was always a feverish stowing of sandwiches into pockets and a pang of regret when the last few dances were beginning and we had to leave the remains of the supper and return to the Hall. We would be tired now, for it was almost ten o'clock, yet our excitement which was fast turning to irritability became renewed when we caught sight of Dr Steward and perhaps Dr Portman sitting in their plush chairs watching and pointing and smiling.

Always when I saw the doctor my heart contracted with suspense, for in spite of the influence of Matron Glass and Sister Bridge it was the doctor's decision which mattered – yet how could he decide if he didn't know you, didn't really know you except to say in Ward Four 'Good Morning,' and in Ward Two, nothing, and listen only to Sister Bridge asserting that what you needed was a lesson to teach you how to behave and pull yourself together, a girl with your education. So when I was whirled in a waltz past the royal dais I would tremble with apprehension and try to dance well, and think 'There's Dr Steward, he's watching me, he's seeing that someone has asked me to dance, that I'm not a wallflower, he's seeing that I'm well, that I needn't be in Ward Two spending all day shut in the dayroom or the yard or the park; he's deciding about me. Deciding now.' But when I came closer to him and dared to sneak a glance at him sitting in royalty there, it appeared that he wasn't thinking about me at all, that he hadn't even noticed me, he was talking to someone, saying 'Yes, I . . . I . . . I . . .'

Of course. Like me, like all of us, he was thinking and talking about himself.

The dance ended, we were lined up in ward groups at the entrance to the hall, and hustled out, with the nurse tapping our shoulder as we passed, counting us. 'Come along or you'll be here all night. Come along. Any more for Ward Two? Nurse, have you got your correct number? Have you checked them?' When we hurried noisily through Ward One some of the children woke up and began to cry at the lights and the hubbub of voices, and some stayed undisturbed, blissful and rosy with sleep. The old ladies stirred and sighed; their beds and their bones creaked. Without ceremony, once we had reached the Brick Building, we were stripped of our party dresses and put into our room or our dormitory and locked in.

I wonder who made the decision to provide us with cakes instead of sedatives or if a choice was ever given. Cakes were plentiful. Almost every night, and particularly the night of a dance or any other official outing there was little hope of sleep amid the screams and shouts and curses. Our noisy return after a dance would awaken the few people in the dirty dormitory who ever slept; the others would continue their raging on a less subdued note. And those returning irritable and tired, not wanting to go to bed and depressed at the thought of tomorrow and the sight of the beautiful party dresses being borne away anyhow by the night nurses acting as cruel bailiffs, were too easily roused to anger and violence.

I huddled in my small room with my head under the bedclothes and my fingers to my ears and my eyes stinging with rejected sleep, and too soon morning came, the blackbirds, the dim light through the closed shutters, and the six o'clock jingling of keys as the nurses unlocked the doors and threw in the clothing bundles. There were fights, clothing was missing, people felt stale and sticky with old make-up on their faces and gaped like clowns at one another in the sorting out of oneself and other people that is part of the difficult routine of emerging from a half-sleep and acknowledging morning. The staff too suffered from irritability. 'No more dances for you my lady, no more dances for you.'

And all day among those who talked the conversation would be of the dance. Brenda would purse her lips and say, 'I saw you last night Miss Istina Mavet, having a wonderful time dancing and dancing. You had such a *dashing* partner. How I wish I were you to have a dashing partner to make my heart beat. Get out of here Mr Frederick Barnes. This instant.'

Eric wasn't 'dashing' and I hadn't been enjoying a 'wonderful time' yet Brenda's attitude to me was always one of sympathetic envy and longing which made me feel responsible for her rescue and for her plight if rescue never came. I was ashamed of my wholeness compared with Brenda's fragmented mind scattered by secret explosion to the four corners of itself. I knew they had tried without success to bore holes in her brain to let the disturbing forces fly out, like leaves or demons from a burning tree. Who could make her whole? Where was the conjurer? I was powerless. I knew only a rotund cleric who might, on persuasion, produce a stream of silk handkerchiefs from a top hat.

* * *

A Sports Day was held each year in February, late summer, when the fresh sea breezes, already seeking signs of decay, combed irreverently through the grass inspecting each withered blade like the young pointing out in public the grey hairs on an aging head, and thumbed each leaf like hired scrutineers counting the votes for death. Often for days on end, out of caution or inertia and the need to gather secret weapons, the season stayed poised in the same weather, bringing a deceptive feeling of timelessness, a separation from time which was, in reality, time's invasion which could not be borne and so was rejected from consciousness and remained monotonously in the background, unnoticed, like a clock ticking or traffic or the sea flowing.

When Sports Day was held at this time it always gave a feeling of shock by its intrusion. One was forced to stop and listen, as when the rhythm of the clock or the traffic or the sea changes; and fear came, as if the bolstering background of time had suddenly dissolved. It seems strange now that so many emotions could be aroused by a mere Sports Day, and that when the season was tired, in dressing gown and pinned hair, so to speak, in preparation for the compulsion of sleep, the mentally ill should be called forth to build a temple glorifying physical power. What did it mean?

Nothing. It was simply Sports Day, another finishing post in a marathon of excitement which had begun weeks before and from which, one by one, the patients who became uncontrollable were dropped out, put in the park or the yard or the dirty dayroom or in seclusion; while Matron Glass and Sister Bridge stood by the side of this track of restlessness and agitation barracking us with cries of, 'No Sports Day for you my lady misbehaving like this. Watch your step or Monday won't see you at the Sports.'

In the week end before the Day the temple and its precincts were marked on the lawn in front of the main door of the hospital: white lines, jumping poles, sandpits, red and white flags cheekily slapping the air; and that Sunday on our walk we saw groups of men patients rehearsing the chief ceremonies – vaulting over poles, jumping in sacks, or limbering up, running on the spot with high knee-raising. They were like little boys who take the field before or after the big game and hope the crowd is watching their exploits; but in this case the men were not imitating the heroes of the hour: they were imitating themselves, and the circle of their isolation was complete.

Watch me. I jump so high I reach the sky.

On Monday we dressed in our party clothes which looked gaudy and incongruous on people about to take part in sports, yet it was the hospital rule that all patients visiting the front of the hospital were to be 'dressed,' as village folk sometimes came as spectators, and on the second day of the Sports the children of the village were given a half-holiday, and a special programme of races, followed by a spree of soft drinks and sweets, was arranged for them.

We stood around in our sweat-smelling creased clothes watching the people from Ward One being lined up by the attendant in his smart black suit with its cuffless trousers like those worn by a policeman, and some of us volunteered to take part, for the longer you had been in hospital the more willing you became to join in festivities that to the uninitiated, like most of Ward Four and the convalescent ward, brought only embarrassment and self-consciousness, so that few of these people could be persuaded to jump about in sacks and knot handkerchiefs around their ankles and run with the men in the three-legged race. As at the dance, they 'wondered what the fuss was about.'

But we in Ward Two and those permanent patients of Ward One, living in a time of prolonged war, moved closer to one another in spite of our separately sealed worlds, like glass globes of trick snowstorms, and we unself-consciously grabbed any pleasures and did not really care if we ran with taffeta dresses tucked into our pants, and were not ashamed to present ourselves for two ice creams, lying that we had been 'missed out' at the time of the first distribution. Someone called through a loudspeaker, 'Women's flat race!' and set my heart thumping with excitement, for after the preliminary exchange, 'You're not bad at running, Istina, why don't you enter?' – 'No, I don't think so.' – 'Why not? Keep up the reputation of the ward.' – 'All right then.' – I knew I would hurry across to the starting point and when the pistol shot sounded, leap into the white-bordered lane and run for dear life though the wind kept blowing in my face and trying to prevent my advance, and I would feel as if I were making no progress over the ground that seemed to shift strangely in heavy clots like wet sand.

Sometimes I snapped first across the tape and hurried breathless and proud, and certain that everyone was admiring me, to the attendant who gave me a card printed in red ink FIRST PLACE; and with the other prize winners, all of us talking together with our words lopping out like white of egg that is in two minds about which globule to join and strays between one and the other, half-fusing with both, I stopped under the flap of the sawdust-smelling tent where the prizes were arranged on trestle tables. Displayed and pleased, we surrendered our tickets. Eric, as one of the trusted patients – and somehow as a natural inhabiter of the small tents that, offering seedy forms of magic, encircle like off-white canvas alps the fairground of a traveling side show – stood behind one of the tables, distributing the prizes.

'I watched you,' he said as he handed me the nylon stockings, first prize. 'Come with me in the three-legged.'

'No,' I replied distantly. 'I've promised Ted.'

Ted was the former Borstal boy who now worked in the Superintendent's garden and helped with the milk cans in the morning. He was stocky and dark and his face seemed always to have an expression of crafty admiration both for himself and for other people. It was the overwhelming desire to touch what he admired that had sent him to the Borstal reformatory. His hands were clumsy and large, like separate people with wills of their own, and to deny them the power to touch would be like denying a sculptor his contact with stone. But Ted was not a sculptor; he was a young man with a love of admiring and of being admired, and his cunning expression arose from his continual need to practise the commerce of admiration in which he had truly invested his life.

On Sports Day he entered for many races, and won, and could not contain his high spirits but leapt about the field getting in everyone's way, and when he came to me, I said yes I would go with him in the three-legged race. We won. I made another journey to the tent to collect my prize.

'I watched you,' Eric said as he handed me the nylon stockings. 'Will you come with me next year in the three-legged?'

Meanwhile the drinks had arrived, not bottled fizz as at the dances but what looked like kerosene tins brimming with blood-colored liquid, a heavy syrupy brew which was distributed in hospital cups and left a red stain inside the cup. We drank and returned for more; we were allowed to drink as much as we liked, and the absence of anyone saying 'Young lady, you've had your whack,' gave us a gaudy feeling of delight and perhaps, on the outskirts of our mind, stirred a slumbering apprehension at the thought of the inevitable aftermath of our makeshift picnic pleasures. Gaily we let ourselves be herded back to the ward for dinner, and were shocked to see that Ward Two had not changed, that people still screamed and cursed in the dirty dayroom, and Sister Bridge still called out, 'Lavatory Ladies!' standing on guard outside the bathroom door.

It is always hard to believe that the will to change something does not produce an immediate change. Why did Ward Two still exist when we had been merrily carousing on the front lawn, filling ourselves with ruby syrup and ice cream in the atmosphere of a fairground? Why did we imagine that because we watched only the stream of silk handkerchiefs, the conjurer was not still practising his skills of deceit, so that in the end we refused to believe in the deceit?

In the afternoon the doctors and their wives and children visited the Sports to watch the races between members of the staff. We ran no more races; we were spectators now, gazing intensely at the strange people who were not patients. We began to feel lonely and depressed as the excitement of our share of the sports faded, as it flowed away leaving the dregs of ordinary routine, Brick Ladies, Lavatory Ladies, Park Ladies. We knew the truth of picnics and dances and sports days, just as a child, after a while, knows the truth when the dentist promises to take away the pain by putting 'a little dolly on a dolly's pillow to sleep in your mouth.'

 11.

The long corridor outside shines like the leather of a new shoe that walks that walks upon itself in a ghost footstep upon its own shining until it reaches the room where the women wait, in night clothes, for the nine o'clock terror called electric shock treatment. They wear dressing gowns of red flannel, as if God or the devil had purchased a continent of cloth and walked, with scissors for stick, from coast to coast, to cut the dead mass pattern of mad men and women whose eyes will spring blind with sight of their world and the flag of cloth hung in the shape of sun across their only sky.

Oh, but at nine o'clock, it is said, all will be well. Their seeing will be blinded, the shade replaced across their eyes to restrict their looking to their plate, their tea, their cigarette; in practice for the world; stopped like a house to look forever on its backyard.

Hairclips have been taken from them and arranged in rows along the mantelpiece. Their teeth are sunk in handleless cups of luke-warm water, arranged in circles, for companionship, upon the bony-legged table.

—Take your teeth out, the women in pink have commanded. Take your teeth out.

And soon the same god or devil who walked the continent of cloth will turn the switch that commands – See. Forget. Go blind.

Be convulsed and never know why.

Take your teeth out as a precaution against choking, your

eyes out, like Gloucester, to save you sight of the cliff and the greater gods who keep their 'dreadful pother' above your head. Your life out as a precaution against living.

And the women, submitting their teeth, their eyes, their lives, smile, embarrassed or mad in their world of mass red flannel.

The nurse is pink, like a flower from the garden, except the wind that bends her body is blown from the same continent of swamp and trapped water with the voice of God or the devil in her ear, like the same small voice that drove the horse, said Gee-up, Whoa.

on the sunniest of days, coloured like a single toi-toi with a sunflower in its heart of seedcake though the seeds were burned black in ash that the same wind that bends and crushes the pink body of flower had driven on and on through a million years to a world of blindness

this room

and a black blanket laid like an elasticised and bordered beetle upon the bed, and the women lying upon its furred shell with their temples washed clean in a purple gasp of liquid *ethereal soap*

concealed in cotton wool. And the gabbling jibbering forest-quiet women wait in crocodile for the switch that abandons them from seeing

and fear

and no struggle to leave for in seeing they inhabit a room of blind where the corridors are moulded lockless, and those who enter from the corridor may cleave the wall with their bodies, and the same wall closes behind them in a velvet mass like a wave in the wake of a journeying saint or ship.

But God or the devil has come, walking the long corridor, squeezing his mind and voice in molecular drops through the forbidding encircling wall. He greets the women. He wrings the blood from their gowns of flannel. It drips upon the floor into a creek flowing to the wall and not passing through and now it is a wave pressing upon the wall and unable to escape.

The women scream. They fear drowning. Or burning.

The nurse picks off one of her pink petals, flutters it upon the wave to soak the crimson, suck it in one breath. Then she readjusts her body, tucking the petal in the gap between her mouth and eyes, and smiles upon God or the devil who stands ready to signal her with a lift of the hand, a widening of his eyes, a signal as secretive as a scream

and the head of the writhing crocodile is broken off, dragged through the door at the end of the room,

and the door flings itself open like two palms which gesture, *Cela m'est egal, Cela m'est egal.*

And the writhing head is borne inside, and the women waiting hear a shuffle of footsteps, a voice, two voices, the scream of a soul being surprised in a funnel of dark. Then silence. Till the door flings itself open again in a gesture of indifference, revealing its wooden hands and the grains of heart and life and fate.

Cela m'est egal, cela m'est egal, it speaks like a carefree breath or commonplace, and the wheeled-out bed holds what is left of the head of the crocodile, whose face is blue, like Toby, with a black pipe like a whistle stuck in its mouth.

Its eyes are open in their triumph of instilled blindness.

Unconscious, the head groans and writhes and quickly, as it would die, it is screened by roses from the rest of the writhing crocodile, and its eyes closed and smoothed with the forefinger of the pink flower, gently, as the dead are treated, who cannot be hurt now; and the pipe taken from its mouth as if, had it lain longer there, it may have played too enticingly its melody of blindness.

And once more the crocodile is severed, the same procession to the door, the same quietness,

Cela m'est egal.

And now Daphne passes the rows of women who lie dead, each with her pipe or whistle thrust in her mouth, or quickly withdrawn in case the music make immobile, as in the fairy tale, the world outside and here.

The doors receive. The same indifference.

And God or the devil on the left, at the head of the raised bed that floats, chequered, like a shadow projected from the tethered real by some invisible globe of light. The doctor moves, carefully, as if he tiptoed between swords. He is guarding something. At first it seems his life. Then it is the machine, cream, with curved body and luminous eyes, one red, the dangerous eye, the other black for cancellation of impulse. He stands with his hand resting lightly, it seems lightly, upon his treasure; then Daphne knows he dare not move his hand away from the voluptuous body of the red and black-eyed machine which, in case of escape, is fastened, as a lover secures the object of his love with cords of habit, circumstance, convenience, time, with black charged cords, varicose, converging to a unity that is controlled by a switch, and pressure of the doctor's own hand.

—Turn on, my love, he will say, and reach for the switch, and caress the red luminous eye with his gentle hand.

He looks at Daphne, as if she may have interrupted his pleasure, or as if he will communicate to her, then blot from her knowing, the delight he feels in his lovely machine.

—Climb up on the bed, Daphne.

She climbs a suspended shadow of mountain and finds on its summit a golden hollow, her own size, for lying in. How well it fits, carved for her comfort, by each year of her life, changed to rain and wind from the north, or the south, bringing snow.

—Lie down, Daphne.

Daphne lies down. Suddenly over the top of the mountain, their heads level with the lowest cloud, there appear the faces, set and shaped in cloud, of five women dressed in white, envying the gold hollow. They look down and smile, to win friendship. Their hands itch to dig the gold, store it in their ample linen pockets and crawl from the room; for they *must* crawl, they are white insects with feelers waving in their heads, each feeler tipped with a trace of white like a separated snowdrop. They wave their feelers.

—Lie down, Daphne.

—Lie down, Daphne.

The doctor comes as close as he dare without drawing his hand from the switch of his love.

—Hello.

He smiles, a wicked deceitful smile, like the world after the morning, that reveals the truth of the golden mountain, of every gold mountain; that all are nests of clay, and the sun an inarticulate rock whose deceptive attribute of light, chipped off by pick-pick of time, closed upon the silence of its unshadow and oblivion.

—Hello, Daphne.

The women wave their feelers. They suddenly go stiff, their knees set like concrete, their breasts of stone; and press icicles upon Daphne's ears, and her body down, down in the hollow; though one of them says kindly,

—Put this in your mouth.

It is not an aniseed ball or acid drop or blackball, but a little black pipe or whistle.

—Bite it.

Should it not be played? Drop thy pipe, thy happy pipe.

The doctor, waiting, exults. He presses the switch. One moment then, and nothing.

12.

A dialogue is not the best way
to contain and capture last Sunday
yet we were two that, unlike the sea-gulls, spoke words.
'Terns churr-churr. That is their sound,' you said. 'Sea swallows
birds with graceful flight diving and soaring like fish in air.
Their tails are like fishes' tails too.'

Under the trees the puppet daffodils shook their heads
nodding agreement to a plan we knew nothing of. Their
applause, approval,
guided by the wind, continued
after we were gone while the dark trees above rocked
slowly, solemn breves to the golden demi-semi-quaver tune.
I thought their heads would be shaken off and roll downhill
into the green valley. It was hard to believe that on a still day

the daffodils stood with heads bowed
in gold shock under their yolk of calm.
You said as you started the car and drove away,
'There may be only a week left in which to see them.
They will be dead soon,'

Dead, over, gone. How we accept it, in flowers!
We come in season to stare and go away murmuring,
'The show is better than ever this year.'

Around the bay the waves were dark, crested with white,
like creatures moving alive under a wide blue blanket
with nobody warning them, Keep still!
Small waves trying to climb too high to see over the heads of
  those in front,
dark periwinkle waves, blue-skirted above a funnel of snow
with the wind sucking the honey of sound through.
Wallflowers along the clay bank, taking a warm glowing hold
with suncolour and smell and (more practical)
with summer root, velvet cloaks wound
buttoned against the inquisitive wind.

And then at the bach around the bay
we stopped to rest and eat and talk
and imagine the city hills misted with dark virgin bush
before you and I and we and they and they came.
We knew how the land appeared then. We remembered
as we remember clearly the world before birth
when waterfalls touched our skin and we grew, thinking, first
we might be a tree or tadpole until the oppression of knowing
surged in us refusing to set us free
from what we had begun to be.
Now only parts of us, like our thoughts, glow, are glossed with
  sun and fall
brittle in shapes of dust
as leaves do, giddy leaves growing first on a green tree.

Sheltered from the sea wind we lazed and looked.

You chuffed a lawnmower over the grass
then served lemonade and crushed orange, measuring fair
levels
in bottle and cup as if it were childhood we had driven back to.
'My favourite toy,' you said, 'was a tea set
kept out of reach, not belonging to me, of blue enamel; I
thought
my heart would burst in its beating when I was allowed to
pour out
tea from the tiny blue teapot with the question-mark spout.
And what was your favourite toy?'

'Mine,' I said, 'was a paraffin tin. I dragged it along in the
grey dust
on a piece of string. It was shining and silver and hollow and it
sang in the sun
and everything that touched it made it sing exclaim groan
tingle cling-clang, gasp a tin gasp, and proclaim
its sound and shape and glossy being
as an empty new paraffin tin that sang and mirrored the world.'

'Everything is always changing.' you said.
'A tree does not want to be anything but a tree.
Hands are better than wings; hands can fly.
Everything changes. The dead clematis on that tree is a burden
to it.
It's like an old man with a sack on his back leaning towards
the sea.
Hear the waves?'

I quoted,
'Palpitation de la mer.' A pulse beat.

'I would fight,' you said suddenly, 'if I were a child and my
toys were taken away.
Would you fight?'

'As a child' I said, 'I had few toys, no favourites. I cared most

for beetles and spiders, small cold creatures that lay
under stones, without sun.'

'How lovely the periwinkle loops along the crisscross wire fence!
And the primrose flowering in the middle of the path. It was out when we came here last. It is not dead yet.
Honeysuckle grows here.
There are four shelves of books in the sitting room. Poetry, the Old Testament.
I should like to stay here in winter, in the wild weather.'

'Would it not be too cold?'

'I should like to stay here when storms come out of the sea, and frostferns work
their stiff embroidery on the windowpanes.'

'Do you keep a diary?'
'I used to. I burned it. Do you keep one?'
'I do. Details I want to remember. Colours. A chance remark. A shape.'
'My diary, years ago, was of love; of smiles given
near and far away as the sun; of passionate beings
out of reach but shining faithfully, like planets.'

'Everything changes. Nothing will stay. My mother died four years ago,
and though I still do not mourn for her, I remember her.
Memory recurs, cripples. There is no relief from its pain.'

'There is no measurement of time.'
'Our parents are our first world. Do you remember
the childhood imagining of their death, of how it would be
with mother and father dead? How cruel winds came in
to take up the space they left, how exposed you stood
as on a headland, and could not bear the grief flowing
down down through your body to draw you into the earth?'

'I had no imaging of it. My mind and heart would not let
me see it.
I closed myself against it like a flower closing against the night.'

'I saw it, Skipping,
Two little girls in navy blue
these are the actions they must do;
salute to the King,
bow to the Queen—
I would stop suddenly because my mother and father were
dead and there was no one above me to bend over me,
there was nothing above me save the sky.
Underchild, underdog, so happily under, and no one now to
intercept
the hawk, the bogie, the charging bull, the glass words of
people, their hooked faces and their wire smiles,
their stiff geometric frowns.'

'No, I never saw it. I would not let myself see it. When the
thought came
I made myself small and hid under a nasturtium leaf
and looked up, full of wise cunning, at the thin green rafters.
Oh, all is changing. All is different. Yesterday, today. Hear the
terns?
Their cry is always churr-churr-churr,
the repetitive deadening sentence;
but our words are not numbered; in crowds they come and
go;
how I wish the few chosen would stay near,
close about us like threaded beads,
restricted like the cry of the tern!

'The day dazzles but is cold. Let us go home now.
It was like this and this now it is not.'

'When people are toys you cannot fight to regain them.
They are gone. Let us put our perplexity and pain
in the sack of dead clematis that the old man tree

swings
  towards
    the sea.'

 13.

Godfrey thinks morbid thoughts all the time now, Beatrice said to Lynley when they were inside the house and had sharpened their claws and begun what both had been longing for and dreading – the 'woman-to-woman' talk. Beatrice had inherited a vague horror of 'morbid thoughts' from her mother whose favourite phrase it had been – 'Don't think morbid thoughts.'

– He'll be better when he's back at work, Lynley said, standing side by side with Beatrice on neutral ground with not a menacing view in sight though the eyes of both were sharpened like pencils ready to censor unwelcome views over personal territory.

– Perhaps we could emigrate, Beatrice said. – Convicted murderers who have been released often do. And other criminals. Even divorcees. Anyone with a scandal to their name. It would be easier to start life in another country where no one knew you.

Lynley coloured. – But Godfrey *has* started life in another country. And I'm starting a life here too. (Godfrey and I are together in this. Surely you're not suggesting we came out here because–)

– Oh no of course not.

The thought had not occurred to Beatrice but once it entered her mind it lingered: thoughts are so hard to come by that any borrowed from elsewhere is always welcome. She looked shrewdly at Lynley, sizing her up: late forties, well-dressed, housekeeper to an elderly gentleman who left her an income. It sounds, Beatrice thought, as though she might have performed some services other than housekeeping for the old chap. These women who housekeep for elderly men. I've heard of them. Glancing again at Lynley she had to admit that here was no old man's darling. The sad irritating fact was that Lynley appeared as she was – Godfrey's sister arrived in New Zealand to attend his funeral and make herself a new home. Beatrice felt new sympathy for Lynley sitting there in all her lack of mystery, her feelings transparent, wanting to own Godfrey and realizing that she couldn't because he belonged now to Beatrice; wanting him to remember his days in England, how she had mothered him, wanting him to revenge himself on those who had declared him dead. It's sad, Beatrice thought, watching her, claws sheathed now she knew there was no danger, that she's not the sort of woman who would be content with cats. Cats are a great standby. She must have Godfrey or some part of him. Why doesn't she join some kind of Union? she thought irritably.

– We're so much at home here though, Lynley. The view is terrific. Be sure you get a place with a view.

There. She had said it. It would do no harm to remind the poor woman that she could not make her life with the Rainbirds.

– That's one of the things I'm thinking of, Lynley said with a touch of pride. – As soon as I get a place of my own I'll move into it. But I feel that while Godfrey is as he is it wouldn't be right to leave him. I mean it would seem as if I were abandoning him.

Beatrice grew impatient. – In what way? How do you mean – *abandoning* him?

Lynley looked vaguely around the room. She saw the shaft of sunlight that fell through the window illuminating in its path the specks of dust, insects, perhaps germs, not normally seen. When the sun shone, however, they could not escape; they danced or drifted into the trap and were exposed for what they were: their real nature showed. – I wouldn't want to abandon him. He needs our support. He could be threatened.

– He'll not be helped, Beatrice said sternly, – As long as he thinks those morbid thoughts.

Lynley looked wise. – The experience itself, she said wisely –

has been – well, morbid, literally. The thoughts merely suit the experience. Besides, how do you know what he is thinking when he's so deep?

Her heart sank as Beatrice said simply, – I know.

– Have you tried religion?

– We weren't brought up to it. Mum and Dad went to church and Bob and I used to go to St Paul's Sunday School until Bob dropped it for football practice. Then Mum and Dad stopped going when there was a crisis with the wallpaper – the new materials coming in. I won a prize for reciting 'The heavens declare the glory of God, the firmament showeth his handiwork, Day unto day uttereth speech and night unto night showeth knowledge.' I used to know it by heart. Beatrice spoke with nostalgic wistfulness of a time she had not really enjoyed. — Why do you ask about religion?

– We used to pray during the War, Lynley said. – We had never been churchgoers but during the War it was different, there was something important to pray for, to keep your mind occupied. Either your prayer was answered or it wasn't but I always feel the more suffering there is the more miracles you've a right to expect. The hymns helped – Eternal Father strong to Save Whose arm hath bound the Restless Wave. Godfrey used to pray as a little boy, she said sharply, waiting tensely for Beatrice to reply.

Beatrice decided not to discuss Godfrey's present habits. Give her an inch she'll take a mile, she thought.

– I thought it might have helped, Lynley persisted bleakly. – Like during the War.

Would they ever forget the War? Beatrice wondered. – This country, she said, is more favourable than any other for his recovery. A pleasant climate. Healthy outdoor life. He gets a good wage, we've plenty to eat, we've our own house. What more could we want?

The list was impressive. Lynley nodded agreement. —What more? she echoed, glancing out of the window at the bright sun-filled sky. – All the same, she said, – What he's been through doesn't seem to fit in with anything here. I mean the sky is so blue. She spoke in a tone of wonder.

What nonsense, Beatrice thought. Surely she's not trying to say that his sufferings would be more widely understood in a country with grey skies! – We're *people* here, you know, Beatrice cried. – Just as you are *people* over there. It's no use trying to compare your country and mine by weighing the burden of suffering with the verdict that the heavier burden gives superiority!

– No I didn't mean that. I *was* thinking of all the tortured and the dead in other countries; but I mean that everything here *caters* for you if you live like everyone else, enjoying a healthy outdoor life, getting a good wage, having plenty to eat, owning your own home. But what if you're not like that? What if you don't like scenery?

Beatrice shuddered at this dismissal of her country's beauty with the word *scenery*. – You'll get to like it, she said. – If you stay long enough.

– But what if you just like it and that's all and decide not to spend your weekends and holidays worshipping it, and what if you don't want a house with a garden, what if you don't mind a flat on the fifteenth floor of an apartment house with a window-box to plant flowers in, if you like flowers?

– Fifteen floors and blot out the sun! Lower the standard of living? You have to fit in here, Lynley, I'll tell you that. Now take Godfrey – She could say that, for she had taken him, in body and soul, for life. – He's fitted in marvellously. He's a real Kiwi and proud of it. Sometimes I have to remind myself that it's only ten years or so since he came out from England. He's popular at work and the men at work are honest who they like and who they don't like. He's quiet, I know. Sometimes they tease him about being so quiet. But he's deep. He doesn't often go out. There's the Fellowship Society – you raise money to send people to your twin city in other lands; he was coming home from it when he was killed.

Killed?

Had they forgotten, to sit here comparing the merits of their countries? A feeling of guilt came over Beatrice. She believed it was her duty to remember the accident; forgetting seemed a sacrilege, like forgetting a birthday or wedding; at the same time she longed to put it out of her mind for ever. – I'm told that clothes are much cheaper in England, she said wilfully straying.

How can she? Lynley thought. With Godfrey out there on the beach. – The dear are dearer and the cheap are cheaper.

– I mean, Beatrice said, – we might just as well talk of clothes.

– If there's anything I can do, anything at all . . . You know how I feel.

The offered range of 'anything' was so wide that Beatrice looked at her with pity. – We'll remember, she said gently, thinking, why, Lynley has come out in gooseflesh on her arm. Godfrey's skin goes that way too. She felt a strong sense of delighted possession at the reminder that she could still move thus, comparing, studying, over the whole of Godfrey's body. – Are you in a draught, Lynley?

Her voice had the generosity the rich feel when they can spare a fur coat for the poor. There was no cold wind blowing yet she asked about the draught for she remembered it was an 'English' habit to have a peculiarly obsessive relationship with draughts. – Shall I put a sausage against the door?

Lynley looked bewildered. Oh it's not fair, she thought. A new land, strange customs, a beloved brother whom she'd flown 'all the way from England' to bury and who now was alive but estranged; and now this coarse foreign language, the absurdity of putting a *sausage* against the door; a native custom perhaps. It wasn't fair of Beatrice to so torment her by introducing unfamiliar words and customs into the conversation. Lynley could feel the pain of longing in her breast. Ponders End. Tooting Bec. Fulham Broadway. Hatfield the North. Slough the West. Wapping. Dorking. Horsham St Faiths.

Then she allowed to happen what she had planned so carefully to avoid – she 'demonstrated' herself, she burst into tears. Apologising, trying to appear brave, she took out her handkerchief and wiped her nose then she mopped the tears that rolled as far as her chin where they were caught and trembling in the hairs there like 'drops on gate-bars hanging in a row'. – I'm sorry, she whispered. – I'm tired.

Beatrice put her arm around her shoulder.

– I'm so tired, Lynley repeated.

Already sensing the mores of her adopted land she knew that tiredness was acceptable, it implied that one had been working, and work was a good and necessary act if one were not to become a charge upon the state; being tired was acceptable; being homesick was not. Homesickness, any strong feeling, was unproductive. If you were homesick you had been moping or you would be, and moping was a crime. The thing to do in this country, to win approval, was to 'get out and about.' Lynley glanced through the window at 'out and about.' – I hope Godfrey is all right, she said. Then she wiped her eyes once more. – I'm sorry, Beatrice. I'm tired.

Beatrice patted her shoulder. – I know. We're all tired. It's the reaction. Next week, thank goodness, we'll be back on the road again.

Though Lynley felt grateful for the sympathy she could not help wincing with distaste at the colonial-sounding phrase Beatrice had used. On the road. As if the Rainbirds were tramps or gypsies. She wished she had never *set foot* (the phrase was so final and personal) in Fleet Drive, Anderson's Bay, Dunedin.

14.

I had been told that spring came early in Las Baleares. Even so, its outbreak of blossom in early January encircled the island with a new bond of sweetness so excessive that it forced dark pleats of pain to be folded within the pleasure.

With the black-and-white beanflower filling acres of fields, the orchards pink and white with colours, never reproduced in paintings, that remain locked within certain flowers, with the spring wind warm, full of the scent of the wild flowers, the almond and avocado blossom, and the beanflowers, I prepared to tolerate the poetry I knew I would try to write in the midst of writing my novel. Often I remembered with a feeling of strangeness that I hadn't spoken English for three months, although I was aware of my English speech tucked away in the corner of my mouth with the key turned in the lock, but I did not realize how rusty with disuse were the key, the lock, and the speech until, arriving home from my walk one afternoon, I met Francesca who repeated excitedly, 'El Americano, El Americano,' while I listened mystified until I saw a tall brown-haired young man coming down the stairs into the sitting room.

He was equally startled to see me.

'Hi,' he said. 'I'm Edwin Mather. I've rented the studio upstairs. I'm a painter.'

I had to search for my English words. (*My* words indeed!)

'I live in the front room,' I said. 'I'm a writer.'

'I guess we share the kitchen and the john outside?'

El Americano. Just as Francesca had warned. Hadn't she told me that she left Algeria because Los Americanos came and took all the oil and perfume?

I felt sick with disappointment and a sense of betrayal for I believed I had rented the entire house and I could not understand how El Patron could now rent other rooms. Perhaps I had been mistaken. I had looked on Number Six Ignacio Riquer as *my place*, shared of course with El Patron and his family and Catalina and Francesca, but not with a *foreigner*, an American painter who spoke English! I felt hostile and unprotected as English thoughts and English words crowded into my head as into an auditorium, each ready to perform its role. There was no-one to appeal to. Number Six Ignacio Riquer had been *my place*.

I recovered a little. At least Edwin Mather would be living upstairs. He would share the house, though, the kitchen, the fire, the front door to the street, the hallway, the sitting room opening on to the patio, the lavatory on the patio, and I'd always be aware of a presence in the house and part of me would be tuned to that presence and distracted from my writing. I felt that the link between the world of living and of writing resembled a high wire needing intense relaxed concentration for the barefoot journey (on knives or featherbeds) between. In such a life the presence of others is a resented intrusion and becomes a welcome joyous diversion only when attention must be directed away from words, if only briefly, during times of travel and sickness.

On this first meeting Edwin and I, like candidates for a post which both had to accept (for he, too, may have thought he had rented the entire house) explained our presence in Ibiza – his funds were from a scholarship which he collected from Andorra where the money market was 'free'. Ignorant of the ways of international currency, I listened attentively as he advised me to change my foreign money in Andorra. He could arrange it, he said.

'Oh,' I said dubiously.

He showed me his studio upstairs, a large airy room with white stone walls, a skylight, and a door opening on to the roof with a panorama of the city, the fields, the ocean, and the mirror city. I felt suddenly disappointed in my restricting of my spirit of adventure – why had I never explored this upper storey of the house? Passing through the sitting room on my way to my bedroom I glanced always at the stone stairway as if it were a place forbidden, without realizing that it was I who had hung out the trespass warning, not aware that I was denying myself a richer view of Mirror City. This revelation of the panorama from the rooftop when I had spent day after day huddled in a rug in my chair in my room, my typewriter on the table before me, my gaze when it strayed from the typewriter fixed only on the mirror city across the harbour, had the effect of an earthquake, shifting my balance, opening depths beneath me, distorting yet enlarging my simple view, as simple as the stare of the blinkered horse I had seen harnessed to circle the well hour after hour, to draw water. No doubt the water was pure and sweet, bearing little relation to the routine of the imprisoned agent working at the well, but I was not so sure that what had appeared on my typewriter was so fresh and sparkling.

Suddenly also I was forced to make a new routine that took account of Edwin. Up early, lighting the fire, I now set aside Edwin's shaving and washing water, and by the time he was out of bed I had breakfasted and begun work. For the evening meal he usually ate with friends at a café or stayed home and cooked his specialty, French onion soup, or shared what was now my specialty, paella with *saffron* which I mention only because I took delight in thinking of myself as 'eating crocuses'. Edwin painted most of the day while I wrote and at times we'd have spontaneous or contrived meetings in the kitchen when he or I asked, 'Quiere el fuego?'

And soon the kitchen shelves became crowded with luxury food that set Catalina and Francesca aquiver with excitement. Edwin's first meeting with them prompted the remark, 'Who are those two old women wandering around prying into everything?'

I explained. Edwin appeared to be unsympathetic towards them while I, who felt that I 'understood' them, sprang to their defence, reminding him that they were poor and could not afford the kind of food he was buying and it was natural for them to help themselves from his bountiful larder.

'But they're wandering in and out all day.'

I told him they lived next door and our fire was their only means of cooking. They had one room, I told him, and they kept bantam hens on a small balcony off their bedroom. 'They might give you a fresh egg now and then,' I said.

He also complained, not unreasonably, about the light bulbs. Although his studio had natural light from the skylight he wanted to be able to paint whenever he wished and to read at night. (I was managing by lighting three or four candles at my table.) Edwin searched the town for new light bulbs which instantly blew the fuses in the house and brought rebuke from Fermin whom Edwin described as 'that interfering little guy with the violin. Have you heard the awful sounds he makes on that violin? I didn't know he would be using this house to practise!'

I pointed to the locked cupboard in the sitting room.

'He has carvings in there. The cupboard lights up when you open the door. He's a sensitive soul.'

Edwin's view of Francesca, Catalina, Fermin, depressed me for to me they were my new family who had looked after me and waited for my luggage to arrive and taught me to shop and cook, and when my three-month visa expired it had been Catalina who had taken me to the police station to introduce me as her friend the writer from Nueva Zelanda who needed her visa renewed. I felt that El Patron and his family needed protection against El Americano. He and his English or American language were the intruders.

For a time I could not adapt to what I saw as the destruction of my perfect world, and I still found writing difficult with a 'presence' in the house, yet gradually Edwin and I began to talk to each other about our work. Each day when he'd finished painting he'd invite me to his studio where he explained his morning's effort and talked about his ideas and art in general, his favourite artists, his life, and in return, although I did not discuss my current work, I lent him a copy of my novel, *Owls Do Cry*, which had now been published and had recently been at the correos when I collected my mail. Edwin liked *Owls Do Cry*. 'It should appear in the States,' he said. He knew someone in New York who worked for a publisher; perhaps he could send a copy there?

I said I'd 'see'.

Apart from professional talk and the phrase spoken often during the day, 'Quiere el fuego,' we lived our separate lives. Then one afternoon when I returned from my walk I was met by Catalina and Francesca in a state of excitement: Edwin had a woman visitor who'd be staying the night . . . in the same room . . . in the same bed. And that evening I met Dora, a flute-player from the mid-West, studying music in Paris. She was small, dainty, with black hair. She wore the 'right' clothes – black *pantalones* and sweater. I longed wistfully to be as full of secrets as she seemed to be, that would prompt a man to discover them, but for so long I had blocked all exits and entrances that I knew or felt that I was as sexless as a block of wood. I had smoothed myself away with veneers of protection.

That evening Edwin and Dora dined out while I, uneasily, with a nagging sense of loneliness and an unwillingness to return to my writing, prepared my self-sufficient meal, read for a while in the half-darkness, looked out dreamily at my Mirror City, then retired to bed. I heard Edwin and Dora come home, laughing and talking as they went up the stairs to his studio, and I felt the sudden unfriendly chill of being just myself and no one else: not dainty but with legs that my sister had said were like footballer's legs, and wristbones that reminded me of railway sleepers.

15.

In the afternoons and evenings I'd tell the children stories using both the French and Spanish versions of 'Once upon a time' – 'Il y avait une fois' and 'Hay en tiempos muy remotos . . .' phrases that always transport me to the mirror world like the Mirror City where civilizations live their lives under the light of the imagination instead of the sun. Lured always by that world and by the fascination of trying to describe it in words that may not even exist for accurate description, from a limited vocabulary, I realized increasingly the extent of its treasure, discovered during visits to the Mirror City where the great artists had lived and returned to describe what they had seen and felt and known. I knew that some had visited and never returned. And here was I with yet another key to the city – 'Hay en tiempos muy remotos', an entrance through the past to the present and the future with stories picked like flowers from the wayside as the traveller moves to and from the City.

As in Ibiza, I became one of the family in Les Escaldes. On Sundays, wearing my black mantilla, I went to church with the family. On Sunday evenings we went to the local cinema where we watched an American film, usually a Western, with Spanish subtitles. And while in the morning I tried to type my book, I was becoming more worried about the pregnancy and myself as the mother of a child: occasionally I was happy, thinking I'd have a replica of Bernard, picturing a boy with Bernard's face and build and laugh, or a girl with his eyes; while of myself reproduced I could see only another fuzzily red-haired Shirley Temple-dimpled child as I had been and I could not imagine Bernard's contribution to another myself. Perhaps, I thought, our grandparents might emerge, effectively cancelling or setting aside our characteristics, or heredity might reach further into the past to retrieve some abandoned trait waiting like a railway coach on a siding to be returned to the main line.

Such romantic dreams were soon dismissed as I recklessly wandered in the mountains, climbing steep slopes, and vaguely wondering about the signs, *Perigo, Danger, Avalanches*. I climbed to the warm lake nestled in the peaks, and I sat gazing down at the dark pines below the snowline, and again I thought of the pines of Ibiza 'que el corazon venera' contrasting them with the dark grief-bowed heads of the pines of Andorra. I passed villages of stone that seemed to be growing out of the rock, huge barns full of cattle, the smell of their manure lingering around the entrance but freezing to nothingness in the mountain breath of the snow. Soon, I was told, the sheep would be driven home through the passes from France where they spent each winter. I learned much about these mountain passes from El Vici who knew the routes by heart and who earned his living, in winter, both as a smuggler and a guide. My naïveté was such that El Vici's smuggling gave him a romantic aura: I never wondered about the nature of the goods smuggled: I simply imagined a group of wild-looking men, El Vici among them, trundling packhorses laden with boxes of contraband across the rugged mountain passes.

After my daily walk I swallowed my quinine tablet as I hoped and denied my hope and grew increasingly fearful and pleased at my condition. It was the need for light that brought a solution to the problem. Although Andorra, unlike Ibiza, had plentiful electricity from the mountain rivers, the inhabitants like Carlos and Donna were too poor to use it and therefore, as in Ibiza, the electric light bulbs were too dim for reading and writing. As Edwin had done in Ibiza (El Americano who 'killed' the light), as Francesca described him, I bought a bulb of higher wattage and standing on a chair, and reaching to change the light to a higher intensity, I became dizzy and sick and fell, and blood flowed reminding me of that first time it had flowed, in the daffodil, snow, World War and birthday time in Oamaru. The blood was bulky. I collected it in a towel and flushed it down the lavatory, pulling the chain several times before it shredded (a quick horror-filled glance told me) and vanished.

Weak and sick I lay in my featherbed and looked at the snow on the mountains.

'You're very pale,' Donna said that evening.

'It's one of those days,' I said.

She smiled, recognizing that we were two women in a male household. I did not realize until the baby had gone that I had accepted it and was preparing for it. I knew a feeling that was stronger than regret but not as intense as bereavement, a no-woman's land of feeling where a marvellous sense of freedom sprang up beside hate for myself, longing for Bernard and what he had given me and never knew, sadness for a lost path, vanishings, with the sense of freedom and the prospect of living a new life in Mirror City, triumphing like the rankest, strongest, most pungent weeds that yet carry exquisite flowers, outgrowing the accepted flowers in no-woman's land.

The physical loss, like widowhood, of Bernard and the loss of the tiny envelope of growth, his 'share', made me turn naturally to accept El Vici's offered company, urged by the delighted Donna and Carlos who already had plans to see us married in the new church. My few days' sickness aroused less attention because the two boys had developed chickenpox and were kept home from school in their darkened room and given drinks of *tisane*.

And in my newly clarified and fused and perhaps con-fused state I accepted El Vici's invitation to go with him for a picnic in the mountains, and so one morning, aware of the approval of Carlos and Donna and of the glances of El Vici's friends along the street, we set out with our picnic along the mountain paths towards the snowline. I had learned that El Vici had been a Resistance worker during the war, later a prisoner in a French concentration camp, and after the war he came to live in Andorra as his knowledge of the mountain pathways was intimate and detailed; in the autumn he picked grapes in the south of France or worked in a fur shop in the south. Like many Italians he was a skilled bicycle racer and so had brought his wonderful blue and white bicycle to Andorra where it was kept in his bedroom, for although he did not ride it, he polished it, oiled it, and turned it upside down on the landing while he spun the wheels and fiddled with the gears. He had given me this information about himself in French which, with Italian and Spanish, he spoke fluently.

I, always an admirer of those with a gift for language, was prepared to like this tall handsome man. I admired his fight against the Fascists led by Il Duce, Mussolini, I sympathized with his suffering and torture in a concentration camp; the fact, however, that I could not accept his wearing of two-tone black and white shoes, and particularly his wearing them in the photograph he gave me, is more a comment on me and the influence of my early life than upon the character of El Vici. In my past and lost world any man wearing 'two-tone' shoes was a 'spiv', a 'lounge lizard', possibly a gangster.

As we walked towards the snow El Vici pointed out landmarks and we talked in French although occasionally we would speak Spanish. We stopped a few yards from the snow that I, enraptured always by snow, heralded with quotes from French poetry in what seemed to me to be an alarming, even a pathetic, repetition of my first walk in Ibiza with Bernard. I felt that I was playing an old record, perhaps my only one, and I thought, would it always be like this, in these circumstances, up and down the same worn pathways of the brain?

As I spread the food on the bare patch of rock, El Vici told how he had been born and brought up in Milano, how his father was a quiet man and his mother was huge in build (he spread his hands apart to depict the width of his mother). He explained that he'd not had 'la bonne chance' with women.

As we began to eat our salami and bread and drink our wine, he suddenly leaned forward to grab at my breasts. I, the prim young woman again, struggled free.

'Oh no,' I said, adopting the manner of a counsellor on affairs of the heart. 'Let's talk about this.' I didn't kiss and cuddle those I didn't know well, I said.

'But you have come walking in the mountains with me,' El Vici protested. 'No woman goes walking in the mountains with a man unless they wish to be lovers.' Women did not go out alone as I did, walking and walking by the river, through the streets, in the mountains. In future, he said, someone should walk with me. He would walk with me and when he was working, Donna and Carlos and the children would escort me. I was Andorran now, he said. Andorra was my home.

El Vici's feelings were more serious than I had gauged. After the day of the picnic he made sure that I did not walk alone, and as it was now the beginning of the Andorran spring, although the road into France was still closed, the mountain flowers were coming into bloom and Donna and the children and I went picking flowers – white violets, primroses, freesias, lilies, their scent still frozen within them by the snowfilled air. I still managed to have my solitary walks, sometimes following the path of the Andorra river or walking into Andorra La Vella to collect parcels sent by Patrick Reilly from England – tins of corned beef, Irish stew, creamed rice, as if I were living in a land of hunger. I had nostalgic letters from Edwin, too. Ibiza was not the same. The old crowd had left, the house was lonely, and Fermin still came to play squeaky music on his violin and the two old servants still pottered around prying into everything and complaining about the terrible crime he was committing by increasing the power of the light bulbs. He had applied for another scholarship, Edwin wrote. Based in Paris. He had not heard from Bernard.

Then one evening when El Vici and I were talking in his room, El Vici suddenly knelt before me, murmuring as he tried to put a ring on my finger, 'Voulez-vous me marier, moi?' The ring, he said, had belonged to his grandmother in Milano.

I was flattered, alarmed, and melancholy, for it was Bernard who still occupied my thoughts and dreams. I realized also that because I'd had the years of my twenties removed from my life I was now behaving in some ways like a woman in her early twenties who had recently left school and home and was exploring for the first time the world of men, women, sex, love. Although I did not accept El Vici's ring, I did not reject him.

Was I prompted perhaps by an impulse of greed, for love at any cost? He and the family therefore concluded that we were 'engaged' and would be married in the church in Andorra. My response had been wait and see. Then, with a sense of panic, I explained that I would first need to return to London where I had 'things to see to' (as if I were arranging my life in preparation for my death), and I would then return to Andorra.

And so it happened again that during the remainder of my stay in Andorra I found myself assuming my most accustomed role, that of the passive person whose life is being planned for her while she dare not for fear or punishment or provocation, refuse. After spending so many years in hospital I was beginning to learn that in the years that followed, this role waited always for me, and much of my life would be spent trying to escape from a prison that I had entered because I was 'used to it and use is everything.'

And so I went walking with El Vici at the proper time for 'promenading'. We attended church, preparing for the late Easter Festival. Donna talked to me of what I would wear at the wedding. Introduced to me, El Vici's friends shook hands heartily and spoke friendly words. And at night curled in my featherbed nest and looking out at the snowcovered mountains behind the buildings of Les Escaldes, I thought of the day's conversation with El Vici, the plans he was making, the answers he gave to my questions, and I felt a chill alarm spreading through me at the prospect of my future life, first in Andorra, then in the south of France working in vineyards, or helping in the fur shop, perhaps living in poverty, trying to take care of *los crios*. I found myself thinking like an 'Englishwoman' going to live in the 'colonies' – 'What about the children's education, the schools?' And what of books, and reading, and my writing? What of music and art? I did not want to become one of the characters that I had seen so romantically as living figures from the paintings of the great artists. Nor did I want to repeat what I had now done several times – used poetry to put myself in human danger and to try to force a flow of love towards me. I was learning that the uses of poetry are endless but not always harmless.

El Vici went with me while I bought a return ticket to London. While he waited outside the travel agency I asked urgently, 'If I don't use the return ticket will my money be refunded?' The clerk assured me it would be.

The Easter celebration was solemnly joyful with the traditional chocolate cake in the shape of a house, the large golden wheel of cheese distributed by the priest from the food parcel from the American government, fondants and biscuits and canalones that I helped Donna make. The table was dressed with a white cloth and candles, like an altar, and even Antoine and Xavier who had been in disgrace for having thrown their Palm Sunday palms out of the window into the street, sat quietly and obediently wearing their white lace collars and their best clothes. Everyone glanced lovingly at everyone else with special glances for El Vici and me, and again I felt myself under the spell of the Spanish and Italian faces with the dark glowing eyes that belonged in the paintings of the masters who 'about suffering were never wrong'. Oh why could I not be there, too, in the painting? I, in spite of my Celtic red hair, my birthplace an Antipodean world where the trees like the pines of Andorra, were a serious evergreen, the colour of eternity, of sovereignty, of the forest ruling naturally with the sea, the sky, the land, the weather. My desire to belong (and how much closer may one be to belonging when one is within both the real city and the Mirror City?) increased my willingness to allow others to decide my life.

That evening I sat in my room, my typewriter balanced on my knee, typing. I heard the murmur of voices as Donna worked with Carlos and the coloured counters. I knew that El Vici was in his room, perhaps polishing his blue and white bicycle. It occurred to me suddenly that I did not know whether he could read or write . . . I was the Englishwoman again among the 'poor peasants' who could never escape while I could escape to London. I thought again of the *crios*, his and mine, loved and wanted but poor, barefooted, unable to go to school – how far did I wish to go, I wondered, in this 'broadening of experience' I had promised to the Literary Fund Committee when I applied for my grant to travel overseas?

And my writing? In a future where I was never alone, where I worked all day picking grapes, caring for children, cooking for my family . . . how could I ever be alone again, able to enter that world of imagination to explore it and try to describe it? Certainly I would be living within it in the world of the old masters but in a world where the cherubs cried and wet their nappies, where bunches of grapes moved and grew and must be picked, in millions, not merely enough to fill a bowl lit by an everlasting shaft of golden light, where dimly lit rooms with all their wonderful play of light and shadow must be lived in, cleaned and repaired and made weatherproof.

And I did not love El Vici: he simply fitted willingly into a vacant space that would soon have its natural overgrowth more suitable to the kind of life I wished to lead.

In mid-May, the very morning the road to France was reopened, I waited with Donna, Carlos, El Vici and the children for the small mountain bus to Perpignan. There were sad farewells, much hugging and kissing and tenderness. No, I told El Vici as we kissed, I would not take his ring with me for perhaps I might lose it. The solemn wise-eyed children who perhaps knew everything (*Cain mató a su hermano Abel*) said their goodbyes. I had bought Antoine a mouth organ with blow-draw instructions; he tried to play a tune for me. I gave Donna my green cortina and the warm brown coat bought for me by my two laughing aunts, Elsie and Joy, mother's sisters. Then, with kisses again for everyone, last for El Vici, I boarded.

The snow lay in two high walls each side of the road. I sat entranced by the blue light, the unreal mountain road brooded over by the snow and the pine trees, and the way that the bus, the first vehicle on the opened road, struggled with its snowplough to clear the path for the snow was falling again. Then, arriving in Perpignan I felt as if I had emerged from a vale of darkness for suddenly the trees were light green, the earth was bathed in a soft cloud of green spring, the *right* springtime. I spent two and a half hours waiting for the train, walking in the village, sitting on the stone seat outside the cemetery, enjoying a luxury of solitude and silence, and the peace, lapped by the desolation of a small wayside station where nothing is coming or going very often, where the posters advertise other places – cities, cathedrals, oceans, other suns and skies full of bright yellow sunlight. I thought of the small railway stations on the main trunk line in the South Island of New Zealand – Winton, Gore, Balclutha, Milton, Clinton . . . and of course walking through the cemetery recalled for me the French poems and prose that were never far from my thoughts . . . 'Qu'il était triste, le cimetière de La Semillante . . . Que je le vois encore avec sa petite muraille basse . . .', sentences that, like music, tastes, perfumes, colours, define and isolate the brooding memories, seeding the clouds, as it were, with pearls. Why do such memories unfailingly return me to my lifelong preoccupation with the sky, with alternating moments of the sun's warmth and the chill and despair of losing the sun and waiting for its return, of a life supervised, blessed and made lonely by the sky?

■ PART TWO

dreams

It is not only in prison that one acts in desperation, puts to personal use the bread of survival, tries to take one by one from the abacus or alphabet the numbers or words to make the shape best suited to the time, the place and the dreams.

('Memory and a Pocketful of Words', p. 487)

I knew (though I was repeatedly urged to 'adapt' 'mix' 'conform') that unless I devoted my time wholly to making designs from my dreams, whether or not those designs were approved or admired, I should spend the remainder of my life in hospital . . .

('Beginnings', p. 46)

16.

It should not have rained. The clothes should have been slapped warm and dry with wind and sun and the day not have been a leafless cloudy secret hard to understand. It is always nice to understand the coming and going of a day. Tell her, blackbird that pirrup-pirruped and rainwater that trickled down the kitchen window-pane and dirty backyard that oozed mud and housed puddles, tell her though the language be something she cannot construe having no grammar of journeys.

Why is the backyard so small and suffocating and untidy? On the rope clothes-line the washing hangs limp and wet, Tom's underpants and the sheets and my best tablecloth. We'll go away from here, Tom and me, we'll go some other place, the country perhaps, he likes the country but he's going on and on to a prize in Tatts and a new home, flat-roofed with blinds down in the front room and a piano with curved legs, though Tom's in the Dye Works just now, bringing home handkerchiefs at the end of each week, from the coats with no names on.

—Isn't it stealing Tom?

—Stealing my foot, I tell you I've worked two years without a holiday. You see? Tom striving for his rights and getting them even if they turn out to be only a small anonymous pile of men's handkerchiefs, but life is funny and people are funny, laugh and the world laughs with you.

She opens the wash-house door to let the blue water out of the tubs, she forgot all about the blue water, and then of all the surprises in the world there's a sheep in the wash-house, a poor sheep not knowing which way to turn, fat and blundering with the shy anxious look sheep have.

—Shoo Shoo.

Sheep are silly animals they're so scared and stupid, they either stand still and do nothing or else go round and round getting nowhere, when they're in they want out and when they're out they sneak in, they don't stay in places, they get lost in bogs and creeks and down cliffs, if only they stayed where they're put.

—Shoo Shoo.

Scared muddy and heavy the sheep lumbers from the wash-house and then bolts up the path, out the half-open gate on to the street and then round the corner out of sight, with the people stopping to stare and say well I declare for you never see sheep in the street, only people.

It should not have rained, the washing should have been dry and why did the sheep come and where did it come from to here in the middle of the city?

A long time ago there were sheep (she remembers, pulling out the plug so the dirty blue water can gurgle away, what slime I must wash more often why is everything always dirty) sheep, and I walked behind them with bare feet on a hot dusty road, with the warm steamy nobbles of sheep dirt getting crushed between my toes and my father close by me powerful and careless, and the dogs padding along the spit dribbling from the loose corners of their mouths, Mac and Jock and Rover waiting for my father to cry Way Back Out, Way Back Out. Tom and me will go some other place I think. Tom and me will get out of here.

She dries her hands on the corner of her sack apron. That's that. A flat-roofed house and beds with shiny covers, and polished fire-tongs, and a picture of moonlight on a lake.

She crosses the backyard, brushing aside the wet clothes to pass. My best tablecloth. If visitors come tonight I am sunk.

But no visitors only Tom bringing cousin Nora, while the rain goes off, she has to catch the six o'clock bus at the end of the road. I must hurry I must be quick it is terrible to miss something. Cousin Nora widowed remarried separated and anxious to tell. Cousin Nora living everywhere and nowhere chained to number fifty Toon Street it is somewhere you must have somewhere even if you know you haven't got anywhere. And what about Tom tied up to a little pile of handkerchiefs and the prize that happens tomorrow and Nance, look at her, the washing's still out and wet, she is tired and flurried, bound by the fearful chain of time and the burning sun and sheep and day that are nowhere.

—But of course Nance I won't have any dinner, you go on dishing up for Tom while I sit here on the sofa.

—Wait, I'll move those newspapers, excuse the muddle, we seem to be in a fearful muddle.

—Oh is that today's paper, no it's Tuesday's, just think on Tuesday Peter and I were up in the north island. He wanted me to sell my house you know, just fancy, he demanded that I sell it and I said not on your life did you marry me for myself or for my house and he said of course he married me for myself but would I sell the house, why I said, well you don't need it now he said, we can live up north, but I do need it I said, I've lived in it nearly all of my life, it's my home, I live there.

Cousin Nora, dressed in navy, her fleecy dark hair and long soft wobbly face like a horse.

—Yes I've lived there all my life, so of course I said quite definitely no. Is that boiled bacon, there's nothing I like better, well if you insist, just the tiniest bit on a plate, over here will do, no no fuss, thank you. Don't you think I was right about the house? I live there.

What does Tom think? His mouth busies itself with boiled bacon while his fingers search an envelope for the pink sheet that means Tatts results, ten thousand pounds first prize, a flat-roofed house and statues in the garden. No prize but first prize will do, Tom is clever and earnest, the other fellows have tickets in Tatts, why not I the other fellows take handkerchiefs home and stray coats sometimes why not I and Bill Tent has a modern house one of those new ones you can never be too interested in where you live. Tom is go-ahead. In the front bedroom there's an orange coloured bed-lamp, it's scorched a bit now but it was lovely when it came, he won it with a question for a radio quiz, his name over the air and all—

Name the planets and their distance from the sun.

Name the planets.

Oh the sun is terribly far away but of course there's only

been rain today, pirrup-pirruping blackbirds, how it rains and the sheep why I must tell them about the sheep.

Nora leans forward, Nance you are dreaming, what *do* you think about the house?

—Oh, always let your conscience be your guide.

(Wear wise saws and modern instances like a false skin a Jiminy Cricket overcoat.)

—That's what I say too, your conscience, and that's why we separated, you heard of course?

Yes Nance knows, from Nora herself as soon as it happened Dear Nance and Tom you'll hardly believe it but Peter and I have decided to go our own ways, you and Tom are lucky you get on so well together no fuss about where to live you don't know how lucky you are.

No fuss but lost, look at the house look at the kitchen, and me going backwards and forwards carrying dishes and picking up newspapers and dirty clothes, muddling backwards and forwards in little irrelevant journeys, but going backwards always, to the time of the sun and the hot dusty road and a powerful father crying Way Back Out Way Back Out.

—Oh, Oh I must tell you, there was a sheep today in the wash-house.

—A what?

—A sheep. I don't know where he lived but I chased him away.

—Oh I say, really, ha ha, it's a good job we've got somewhere to live, I in my house (even though I had to break with Peter) and you and Tom in yours. – We *have* got somewhere to live haven't we, not like a lost sheep ha ha. What's the matter Tom?

—74898, not a win.

The pink ticket thrust back quickly into the envelope and put on the stand beside the wireless, beside the half-open packet of matches and the sheaf of bills and the pile of race-books.

—Well, I'm damned, let's turn on the news, it's almost six.

—Oh it's almost six and my bus!

—So it is Nora.

Quick it is terrible to lose something for the something you miss may be something you have looked for all your life, in the north island and the south island and number fifty Toon Street.

—Goodbye and thank you for the little eat and you must come and see me sometime and for goodness sake Nance get a perm or one of those cold waves, your hair's at the end of its tether.

Here is the news.

Quick goodbye then.

Why am I small and cramped and helpless why are there newspapers on the floor and why didn't I remember to gather up the dirt, where am I living that I'm not neat and tidy with a perm. Oh if only the whole of being were blued and washed and hung out in the far away sun. Nora has travelled she knows about things, it would be nice to travel if you knew where you were going and where you would live at the end or do we ever know, do we ever live where we live, we're always in other places, lost, like sheep, and I cannot understand the leafless cloudy secret and the sun of any day.

17.

People live on earth, and animals and birds; and fish live in the sea, but we do not defeat the sea, for we are driven back to the sky, or we stay, and become what we have tried to conquer, remembering nothing except our new flowing in and out, in and out, sighing for one place, drawn to another, wild with promises to white birds and bright red fish and beaches abandoned then longed for.

I never conquered the sea. I flew at midnight to the earth, and in the morning I was made into a human shape of snow.

'Snowman, Snowman,' my creator said.

Two sharp pieces of coal, fragments of old pine forest, were thrust in my face to be used for my eyes. A row of brass buttons was arranged down my belly to give me dignity and hints of fastenings. A hat was put on my head, a pipe in my mouth.

Man is indeed simplicity, I thought. Coal, brass, cloth, wood – I never dreamed.

* * *

When I looked up at the sky I could see nothing. Yet I felt my body shuddering and the familiar tears ran down my cheeks, and then in a sudden gust of wind something whirled about me, up and down, then out the gate, onto the pavement, into the pool of black blood, then toward me again, round and round my feet and then up to my head where flip-flop-flap it settled and the gust of wind vanished. I was grateful for the shelter upon my head because I was afraid to look too long at the sky in case I saw the sun, though I scarcely knew how I should recognize it.

'My head is protected now. I have shelter. I cannot even see the sky now.'

'You are not the only one to seek shelter from a newspaper; it is common practice. People use it to protect themselves from the weather, others use it to hide from history or time or any of those inconvenient abstractions which man would destroy if only they had a visible shape for him to seize and defeat. Oh these abstractions, Snowman, they are among the most intrusive companions. They are never satisfied unless they have built a nest on the tip of a man's tongue, in the keys of his typewriter, in the hollow of his pen-nib – all favorite places for abstractions to breed and overpopulate the world of words. Even in my talking to you I cannot help mentioning them. Time, I say. Time, History, change. But Time is surely not an abstraction, I think he is a senile creature who is blind because his eyes have been gouged out by an historic fire; his flesh is covered with fur and he licks the hours and swallows them and they form a choking ball inside him. Then Time dies. Time. Death. It is no use, Snowman. The proper place for abstractions is in a region of the mind which must be entered in nakedness of thought. Certain abstractions are powerful and may be lethal yet the way to approach them is not to carry weapons of personification but to act as soldiers do when they surrender, to discard all the known means of defence and retaliation and walk naked toward the hostile territory. Surprising things may happen then, Snowman. We may see abstractions in their truth.

'Truth, death, time, it is no use. How grateful I am that we are made of snow! People need to burn off the old words in the way that a farmer destroys the virgin bush to put the land to new use with controlled sowing and harvesting. I will not say, though, that all such farmers are successful. Their enthusiasm wanes, the crops fail, noxious weeds take the place of the former harmless ones, there are downpours, droughts. And there are always the earliest settlers who yearn for the time when the land was covered with familiar bush and the streams were not dammed to create inexplicable hydro works, and the tall known trees were starred with centuries-old white clematis. But Snowman, Snowman, perhaps words do not matter when it is only a question of surviving for one season. Then the word *Help* is vocabulary enough. Snowmen and Perpetual Snowflakes have no need of words. Snowman, Snowman, look at the gap in the sky. It is the sun.'

'I can see nothing while I wear this torn newspaper over my head. I can see only words in print as you have explained to me. Not *help, help*, but said Mrs Frank Wilkinson in charge of the unit I suppose they have seen some deaf and dumb people on buses and in the street and felt sorry that nobody could talk to them the boys admitted breaking into a prefab for food my girlfriend is a nurse and he made her stand in the snow waiting for me to come home before he would let her in made as new suspects arson her behaviour seemed quite out of character the role of the church is to provide this not to bribe them into attending they want real religion choice of two modern suites for happy holidays licensed bar dancing not guilty are you hard of hearing you lovers' dream home gas death two sides to him you've had your last chance I'm going to sentence you snowdrops are flowering and crocuses are showing in some places so get ready for spring planting if digging hasn't been done get it over quickly leave large lumps for the weather to work on we can still expect frost and snow fire destroys home heater blaze carpet linoleum were destroyed he woke to the smell of burning planned with you in mind luxury in the sun on the sands by the sea the summer of your dreams stretch black threads or the new nylon web over primula or polyanthus buds before the birds get at them planting can start soon for fruit trees fruit bushes roses he'd finished his lunch when someone rang to tell him it's your shop on fire an unknown young boy discovered the fire he was walking past the shop when he thought he saw smoke or steam in the window monster sale end of season. . . .'

I was beginning to wish that I did not know how to read my newspaper shelter. It seemed full of references to fire and sun and spring, and I thought it strange that human beings should also be afraid of fire and sun and spring, so afraid that they had to keep writing of them in newspapers in order to dilute their fear. Two sides to him? What did it mean? And the picture of the sun puzzled me. I could see the caption clearly – Follow the Sun – and at first I was foolish enough to believe that if I looked at a picture of the sun it would have the same effect upon me as if I looked at the sun itself. The sun was portrayed as a semicircle with tentacles growing from it, and a wide smiling mouth. What had I been afraid of? So this was the sun, the picture of benevolence; it had not even eyes to see me. Perhaps the smile was too wide giving its face a suggestion of falseness but there seemed to be no doubt about the sun's kind nature.

'Do these newspaper shelters often happen to snowmen?'

'You are a fool of course. As self-centred as any human being. You imagine that newspapers are printed to shelter you from the sun.'

'I don't need shelter from the sun. I have seen its kind face.'

'It is worse, Snowman, when you are deceived by your own deceit. Newspapers do make convenient shelters for snowmen; also for cooked fish, dog-meat, and they are useful as blankets for tramps; they protect people from the hot and cold weather; they deaden sound; they are the body and tail of kites, and are made into little dishes with flour-and-water paste; they are the heads of puppets, the bed for the cat to have kittens on; they are wrappers, concealers, warmers; also they bring news, even from Rome, Paris, Marseilles.

'Now a gust of wind is blowing near you, Snowman, and for your sake I hope it does not remove your newspaper shelter for when the sun shines it leans close to the earth and the snow is drawn from the earth like white milk from a white breast and when all the snow has vanished and the sun is satisfied the earth lies dry, wrinkled, folded with a dull brown stain spreading through its skin, but you will never see so much, Snowman, nor the change that follows, it is other seasons.'

The gust of wind came near me but it did not blow away my newspaper shelter, and toward evening the tears stopped flowing down my cheeks and a cloud of snow fell from the sky but I could see nothing until a blackbird, going home, stopped to rest on the tree, and seeing me standing forlorn, thin, blind, with the world's news clinging to my stone skull, he flew down and pecked at the newspaper, just a slight stab with his beak, tearing a hole in the paper so that once more I could look at the world with my coal-black pine-forest eye. The blackbird had pierced the word *snowdrops*. When I looked out through the gap in *snowdrops* I could see the blackbird disappearing over the roofs of the buildings and thus I could not ask him whether it was joy or sorrow which had impelled him to stab the chosen word.

Tonight I shall sleep deeply. I feel safe. More snow-armies are arriving upon the earth and all will be as it was on my first day. Snow repairs, cushions, conceals; knives have no blades, mountains have no swords, the yellow earth-cat has white padded claws, and it is people only, those bone-and-flesh scissors snapping in the street, refusing the overcoat of snow which their shadows wear, sneaking faithfully beside them, it is people who change and die. People and birds.

There is a sound at my feet. Something has fallen from the sky. It is not a snowflake, it is a blackbird and it is dead, I know, for I have learned the dispositions of death. Its beak is half-open and quite still and no living blackbird has such a thrust of beak unless it is taking food or attacking the enemy.

Its feathers are ruffled about its neck, its body is huddled, and no living blackbird has such an appearance except in a tree in the wind and rain and now that the snow-armies have arrived for the night the wind does not blow, the tree is still, and there is no rain – but what is rain? How quickly I have learned to gather the clues of death! The bird's claws have as much grasping power now as loose pieces of string. Death has stolen the black sheen of his feathery overcoat and there are two round white pieces of skin like tiny portholes fitted and closed over his once bright watchful eyes. There is a snowdrop lying beside him; its neck is twisted and a green liquid oozes from the crushed stem.

'Snowman, Snowman, there is a gap in the sky.'

My sleep is disturbed tonight. I think I must have dozed several times. My newspaper shelter keeps flapping against my face, it seems to have lodged forever upon my head, and I do not really care to harbour or be protected for too long by stale news two sides to him you've had your last chance I'm going to sentence you snowdrops are flowering and crocuses are showing in some places so get ready for spring an unknown boy discovered the fire he was walking past the shop when he thought he saw smoke or steam in the window nobody could talk to them he felt sorry for them because nobody could talk to them they were deaf and dumb.

Stale news. Yet how can I tell whether news is fresh or stale? When the Perpetual Snowflake talks to me of people he brings centuries-old news that is fresh to me, and the stale news of the prompt arrival of each morning brings with it the excitement of fresh news.

A prowling cat has torn the dead blackbird to pieces and eaten him. It is so dark now. I think I will sleep but I am afraid, why am I afraid, I am only a snowman, your last chance I'm going to sentence you two sides to him snowdrops are flowering and crocuses are showing in some places luxury in the sun on the sand by the sea but we do not defeat the sea for we are driven back to the sky or we stay and become what we have tried to conquer, remembering nothing except our new flowing in and out in and out, sighing for one place, drawn to another, wild with promises to white birds and bright red fish and beaches abandoned then longed for.

'Snowman, Snowman.'

Man is simplicity itself. Coal, brass, cloth, wood.

I never dreamed.

18.

This is a story which belongs in the very room in which I am typing. I am not haunted by it, but I shall tell it to you. It happened once – twice, thrice? – upon a time.

A young man was so bedevilled by the demands of his body that he decided to rid himself of it completely. Now this worry was not a simple matter of occasional annoyance. As soon as the man sat down to work in the morning – he was a private student working all day at this very table with its green plastic cover, drop ends, two protective cork mats – he would be conscious perhaps of an itch in his back which he would be forced to scratch, or he would feel a pain in his arm or shoulder and be unable to rest until he had shaken himself free of the pain which would then drop to the carpet and lie there powerless and be sucked into the vacuum cleaner on a Thursday morning when the woman came to clean the house.

Sometimes as the pain lay upon the carpet the man would engage it in conversation; there would be a lively exchange of bitterness and wit, with the man assuring his pain that he felt no ill-will toward it but he wished that its family would cease inhabiting his body just as he was beginning work for the day. But the pain was cunning. It gave no message to its family which returned again and again, and when it was successfully disposed of by the vacuum cleaner and the County Council Dustmen and transported to a County Council grave, another family of pain took its place.

'I must get rid of my body,' the man thought. 'What use is it to me? It interferes with my work, and since my work is concentrated in my head I think I shall get rid of my body and retain only my head.'

Ah, what freedom then!

There was another difficulty. As soon as the young man wanted to begin his work in the morning, all the feelings which he preferred to inhabit his head to nourish and revive his thoughts, would decide to pack their picnic lunches for the day, and without asking permission, they would set out on the forbidden route to the shady spot between the man's legs where his penis lived in a little house with a red roof, a knocker on the front door, and two gothic columns at the front gate. And there, in the little house in the woods, with the penis as a sometimes thoughtful, sometimes turbulent host, the man's feelings would unwrap their picnic lunch and enjoy a pleasant feast, often sitting outside in the shade of the two gothic columns. And how ardently the sun shone through the trees, through the leaves, in a red haze of burning!

Now you understand that the man became more and more distressed at the way his body demanded so much attention. It had also to be washed, clothed, warmed, cooled, scratched, rubbed, exercised, rested; and should it suffer the slightest harm, pain, like a dragonfly, would alight at the spot with its valise full of instruments of torture which dragonflies used to carry (once, twice, thrice upon a time) when they were the envoys of genuine dragons.

The man grew more and more depressed. He felt himself becoming bankrupt – with his feelings engaged hour after hour in extravagant parties which took no account of the cost, so that bills mounted and could not be paid, and strange authorities intruded to give orders and confuse the situation. And with so little work being done the man did not know where he would find money for rent and food. Sometimes he was so depressed and alone that he wept. His feelings did not seem to care. Whenever he glanced at the little house in the woods he could see at once that all the lights in the house were blazing; he could hear the boisterous singing at night, and witness the riotous carousing during the day under the melting indiarubber sun.

'What shall I do?' the man cried when he woke one morning feeling tired and discouraged. 'Shall I rid myself of my body?'

He decided to rid himself of his body, to keep only his head which, he was convinced, would work faithfully for him once it was set free.

Therefore, the same morning, feeling lighthearted and singing a gay song, the man sharpened his kitchen knife which he had bought at Woolworth's for two and eleven and which had grown blunt from much use as a peeler of vegetables, spreader of marmalade on toast, cutter of string on mysterious packages from foreign countries, whittler of wood on pencils; and, unfolding a copy of the *Guardian*, the man lay it on the kitchen floor, leaned forward, applied the knife to his throat, and in a moment his head had been cut off and the blood was seeping through the Editorial, Letters to the Editor, and the centre news page.

The problem which confronted the man's head now was to get rid of the body, and to clean the blood from the kitchen floor. The head had rolled, its face rather pale with the excitement of its new freedom, as far as the fireplace. Now the man knew of three little mice who lived behind the screen which covered the disused fireplace, and who emerged on expeditions during the night and during the day when they supposed that all the people in the house were at work. The three mice had survived many attempts to kill them. One of the lodgers from upstairs had shaken three little heaps of poisoned cereal on a strip of hardboard in front of the fireplace and had waited in vain for any sign that the mice had been tempted. She did not know that the young man had warned them. He had been in the kitchen one evening making himself a cup of tea, and he was just about to take a slice of bread from his wrapped sliced white loaf when he saw one of the mice sniffing at the poisoned cereal.

'I wouldn't eat it, if I were you,' the young man said. 'Appearances are deceptive you know. Even I have to be careful with every slice of my wrapped sliced white loaf.'

'Why are you warning me?' the little mouse asked. 'Don't

you want to poison me? I thought everybody wanted to poison little mice like me.'

'Don't touch that heap of cereal,' the young man said melodramatically.

The mouse was formal. 'I am grateful sir,' he said, and disappeared.

But naturally the mice were grateful, following the tradition of all rescued animals in fairy stories, and as the young man had indeed been living in a fairy story of despair he had no difficulty now, when he had freed himself from his body, in asking and receiving help from the three mice. They were willing to dispose of the body and to clean the kitchen until the floor was without a trace of blood. In their turn, the mice asked the help of the dustbin downstairs, and because the dustbin had often acted as a gay restaurateur serving delectable suppers to the three mice, and because he did not wish to lose his reputation – for reputations are valuable property and must be stored in a safe place (the dustbin kept his just inside the rim of his grey tin hat) he agreed to come into the house, climb the stairs, remove the body, help to clean away the mess, and put all the refuse and the information concerning it, beneath his tin hat. And all this he accomplished with swiftness and agility which won praise and applause from the three mice. Also, with a kindly impulse, the dustbin carried the man's head to his room and even gave it lessons in flying, for the dustbin lid was a relative of the flying carpet and knew the secrets of flight, and that was why he had been so agile in climbing the stairs and moving in and out of the kitchen.

How patiently he taught the head to fly! He waited so courteously and sympathetically until the art was mastered, and then bidding the head goodbye returned downstairs (conscious of his new reputation as a hero), out the back door, to his home in the tiny backyard where he lived in the company of a shelf of plant pots and a string bag of clothes pegs which continually quarrelled amongst themselves about who were superior, the plastic clothes pegs or the wooden clothes pegs. These quarrels were all the more bitter because they took place among the older generation of clothes pegs; the younger had forgotten or did not know how to quarrel; they were intermarrying and shared shirt flats on the same clothes line; together they topped the country spaces of blankets, and holidayed near the ski slopes of sheets and pillowcases. . . .

Meanwhile, upstairs, the head was flying rapturously to and fro in the bed-sitting-room, and it continued thus in wild freedom all morning and afternoon.

Once it stopped flying and looked thoughtful. 'Am I a man?' it asked itself.

'Or am I a head? I shall call myself a man, for the most important part of me remains.'

'I'll have one day free,' the man said, 'to think things over, and then I'll start my intellectual work with no dictation or interference ever again from my presumptuous imperious body. Oh I feel as if I could fly to the sky and circle the moon; thoughts race through me, eager to be set down upon paper and studied by those who have never had the insight or strategy to rid themselves of their cumbersome bodies. My act has made my brain supreme. I shall work day and night without interruption. . .'

And on and on the man flew, round and round the room in his dizzy delight. Once he flew to the window and looked out, but fortunately no one in the street saw him or there might have been inquiries. Then in the evening, to his surprise, he began to feel tired.

'It seems that sleep is necessary after all,' he said. 'But only a wink or two of sleep, and then I daresay I shall wake refreshed.'

So he lay down beneath the top blanket of his bed, closed his eyes, and slept a deep sleep, and when he woke next morning his first thought almost set him shouting with exhilaration, 'How wonderful to be free!'

That morning the landlady remarked to her husband,'The man in the upstairs room seems to have gone away. I'm sure he did not come home last night. The room is so quiet. His rent is due this morning, and we need the money. I'll give him a few days' grace, and then if we are not paid we shall have to see about finding a new lodger – for this one doesn't seem to do any work really, does he? I mean any real work where you catch the bus in the morning and come home tired at night with your *Evening News* under your arm, and you are too tired to read it.'

Also that morning the woman lodger remarked to the other lodger who lived in the small room upstairs, 'The man who shares the kitchen with us has not used his milk – see it's still in the bottle. I was curious and peeped in the door this morning (I was only wondering about the milk, it might go sour, in this heat) and his bed is unruffled, it's not been slept in. Perhaps I should tell the landlady. She likes to know what goes on. He seems to have vanished. There's no sign of him.'

'Ah,' the man was saying at that very moment as he flew about the room, 'I don't need to eat now, yet I am full of vigour and excitement. My former despair has vanished. I will start work as soon as I hear the two lodgers and the landlady and landlord bang the front door as they go out on their way to work.'

He heard the two lodgers in the kitchen, washing up their breakfast dishes. He heard the landlady putting her clothes through the spin-drier. He heard the landlord go out and start the car.

Then he heard the front door bang, once, twice, three, four times. The house was quiet at last. The man gave a long sigh of content, and prepared to work.

The house was indeed quiet. In the kitchen the three mice emerged from their hiding place to explore and examine the turn of events, for events are like tiny revolving wheels, and mice like to play with them and bowl them along alleyways of yellow light where dustbins glitter and the hats of dustbins shine with pride in their distant relation, the Magic Carpet...

The three mice pattered around the kitchen, and then curious about their friend who had rid himself of his body, they came – one, two, three – into the man's room where they were surprised to observe, on the green plain of the table, the man resting in an attitude of despair.

'Alas,' he was murmuring. 'Where are my fingers to grasp my pen or tap my typewriter, and my hand to reach books from the shelf? And who will comb my hair and rub the hair tonic into my scalp? Besides, my head itches, there is wax in my ears,

I need to keep clearing my throat; how can I blow my nose with dignity? And as for shaving every morning, why, my beard will grow and grow like clematis upon a rotten tree.' Tears trickled from the man's eyes.

The three mice felt very sad. 'We could help you,' they suggested, 'by bringing books to you; but that is all. You need arms, hands, fingers.'

'I need much more,' the man replied. 'Who will listen to my words and love me? And who will want to warm an absent skin or picnic in a deserted house, in darkness, or drink from rivers that have run dry?'

'Still,' the man continued, 'my thoughts are free. I have sacrificed these comforts for my thoughts. Yet although I am no longer a slave to my body I am even now subject to irritations. My vanity demands that I rub hair tonic into my scalp to postpone my baldness, for baldness comes early to our family. My need for relief demands that I scratch a spot just above my right ear. My training in hygiene insists that I blow my nose with a square white handkerchief which has my name – Man – embroidered in one corner! Oh if only I could escape from the petty distractions of my head! Then I would indeed do great work, think noble thoughts. Even my head offends me now. If only I did not possess my head, if I could rid myself of it, if I could just keep my brain and the protective shell enclosing it, then surely I could pursue my work in real freedom!'

Then the idea came to him. Why not ask the mice to fetch the knife from the kitchen (they could carry it easily, one taking the blade, the second the handle, the third acting as guide) and remove all parts of my head except the little walnut which is my brain? It could easily be done. If the mice hurry, the man thought, and set my brain free, no one knows what great work I might accomplish even today before the sun goes down!

So the mice offered to help. They performed the cutting operations and once again the dustbin and the dustbin lid agreed to collect and conceal the remains. Then, when the task was finished the mice lay what was left of the head, upon the table, and silently (for the man could not communicate with them any more) they and the dustbin and the dustbin lid went from the room, the mice to their corner by the fireplace, the dustbin to his place beneath the shelf where the pot plants lived and the older generation of plastic clothes pegs and wooden clothes pegs continued their quarrels in the string bag where they lived.

Blind, speechless, deaf, the man lay upon the table beside his blank writing paper, his books, his typewriter. He did not move. No one could have divined his thoughts; he himself could no longer communicate them.

That night when the lodger returned from work she peered into the room, and seeing no one there, she reported the fact to the landlady who only that afternoon had replied to inquiries for a rented room.

'The man must have flitted,' the landlady said, opening the door and gazing around the room. 'The bed has not been slept in. His luggage is still here. But I think he has flitted because he could not pay his rent. I think he was the type. No regular work. No getting up in the morning to catch the bus and coming home at night with the *Evening News* in his pocket and being too tired to read it.'

Then the landlady gave a slight shiver of anticipation. 'Now I can come into the room and scour it out, wash the curtains, clean the linoleum and the chair covers, redecorate. I'll move the furniture, too, repair the damages he is sure to have done – look, no castors on the chairs, and the spring of that armchair broken, and the cord hanging from the window, and look at the soot on the window sill!'

Then the landlady glanced at the table and noticed the shrivelled remains of the man.

'Just look!' she exclaimed to the lodger. 'An old prune left lying around. Eating prunes no doubt while he worked; or pretended to work. Such habits only encourage the mice. No wonder they haven't been tempted by the poison I left out for them if they have been living on tidbits from this man!' And with an expression of disgust the landlady removed the deaf, blind, speechless, wrinkled man, took him downstairs and threw him into the dustbin, and not even the dustbin recognized him, for he could never any more proclaim his identity – Man; nor could he see that he was lying in a dustbin; nor could he feel anything except a roaring, like the sound in an empty shell which houses only the memory of the tide within its walls.

And the next morning when the three mice were up early and down to the dustbin for breakfast, one saw the shrivelled man, and not recognizing him, exclaimed, 'A prune! I've never tasted prunes, but I can always try.' And so the three mice shared the prune, spitting out the hard bits.

'It wasn't bad,' they said. 'It will do for breakfast.'

Then they hurried downstairs to hide while the landlady who was not going to work that day prepared the man's empty room for its new tenant, a clean businessman who would work from nine till five and bring inconvenience upon no one, least of all upon himself.

19.

Words, first words, are as traumatic as first love and first death. When we are young, presented with mature experienced words and lacking the mental imagery to receive them, we hospitably give them what we have in our minds only to find that we have invited them to live a falsehood which we believe to be truth. I am reminded of a word which caused much hope and suffering to me in my earliest years and which has accompanied me through my life, and because of its privileged metaphorical status, it will also attend my death. It is among the aristocracy of language because we have chosen to put it there.

The word is *jewel*.

I first heard the word 'jewel' when I was very young and its meaning was immediately clear, with the word becoming its meaning. Precious, a treasure, a glittering gem or stone in a choice of many colours and shapes and textures.

I knew that I would never own a jewel. I learned the names of jewels: ruby, sapphire, topaz, carnelian, fire opal, agate, moonstone, bloodstone, jasper, diamond. When my mother, in a poetic frame of mind, glanced out of the window in the early morning and observed that the lawn was covered with jewels I learned not to take her remark literally; nor when she spoke of a relative or friend as being a 'jewel', though I found it hard to accept these falsehoods and I resented the confusion I felt over my inability to discern where to put a word when it was given to me, whether among the real or the unreal, especially when to me all was real. I could say that by the time I was seven I had almost an open mind about language; I was prepared for any shock, and as vigilant as a soldier on sentry duty in my encounters with words, yet I was caught unawares at school one day, in my eighth year, when I overheard a fellow pupil say to his friend,

'In Class Two they sit in *jewel* desks. Class Two is the only classroom with *jewel* desks.'

You may imagine the effect of this news. From that moment I switched my hopes from dreams of Olympic glory (I was a fast runner) to those of acquiring a fortune in jewels. *Jewel desks.* In my saner moments I could not believe it was possible. My curiosity about the room with the jewel desks became intense and as I was too shy to ask for details I had to live in a torture of wondering, with at least the consolation that when I was promoted to Class Two my curiosity would be satisfied. When I passed the door to Class Two it was always closed, and I could hear murmurs from within, which I interpreted as murmurs of wonder and pleasure as Class Two inspected the jewels in a special hour devoted to jewel inspection and appreciation.

It began to seem impossible that I could live through the remaining three months of the year until I became eligible to share the jewels. I had a growing fear that the supply might end, as no doubt the jewels were distributed to Class Two pupils, on loan or permanently; I noticed some bulky schoolbags being carried home in the afternoons. Also, I was worried about the evident secrecy. Except for that one day when I overheard the news I heard no one speak of the jewel desks. Once, casually, making it half a question, half a statement, I said to another boy, 'In Class Two you sit in a jewel desk.'

'Yeah,' he said. 'A jewel desk.'

He was uninterested, or he appeared to be; perhaps he had his own plans about the jewels and was confiding in no one.

One day when school was out and I was late going home I walked along the corridor and I was about to pass the room when I noticed the door was open, and with an awful racing of my heart, I peeped in. I saw the desks, not single desks like ours, but long heavy desks with two lift-up seats to a desk. Not a jewel in sight. Obviously, they were removed each afternoon and locked in the class cupboard, and as if to confirm this, there was the teacher at that moment turning the key in the class cupboard. I had just missed seeing the jewels! It was almost as thrilling as having seen them.

Still, I might have gone crazy with wondering and planning had I not had an unexpected good fortune. One day, on the strength of being Excellent in Comprehension, Spelling and Arithmetic, and being able to recite unfalteringly in their correct order the ten longest rivers, highest mountain peaks, deepest lakes in the world, I, and Gloria Bone, were promoted to Class Two.

'You can move your books after school,' the teacher said. 'And go to Class Two tomorrow.'

After school we took our books to Class Two where, as I expected, the jewels were already locked away for the night.

'We'll be sitting in jewel desks,' Gloria Bone said, so loudly that I hushed her.

'What do you mean, Sh-sh-sh? Everyone knows you sit in jewel desks in Class Two.'

I was alarmed. I saw my fortune disappearing. I dug Gloria Bone with my elbow which was effectively sharp. 'Blabber,' I said.

The teacher took our promotion cards to the class cupboard, opened it, put the cards quickly inside, and relocked it, seeming, to my inflamed imagination, to glance significantly at me as she turned the key in the lock. Her glance promised, Distribution for new pupils of sapphires, diamonds, rubies, carnelian, bloodstone, immediately after the Lord's Prayer and Hymn Singing tomorrow morning. What a stupendous promise! Nothing, I thought, must be allowed to interfere with the distribution of the jewels. Perhaps there would be a special hymn for the occasion,

When he cometh, when he cometh
to make up his jewels,
all his jewels, precious jewels,
his loved and his own . . .

Or perhaps we would sing that hymn where the reckless (how reckless!) saints were 'casting down their golden crowns around the glassy sea.'

There's a limit to patience. When I had been three days in Class Two and there was still no sign of the promised jewels I decided to ask about them. I said to my neighbour who sat with me in the new type of desk,

'I thought these were meant to be jewel desks.'

His reply mystified me. 'They *are* jewel desks. Can't you see?'

Here was a problem. It had not occurred to me that the jewels were invisible, the kind you read about, which could become visible if you were good, clever, self-sacrificing, courageous. Reluctant to admit that I might be none of these, I tried a new approach.

'Are you ever allowed to take them home? You know – a handful – to . . . to . . . (I was about to say to keep or to spend when I suspected this might be classified as unself-sacrificing) you know, to give to your mother so she can see again, or to your father so he can voyage round the world in his spare time.'

My classmate was matter-of-fact. He closed the lid of his desk carefully.

'I didn't know that your mother was blind or that your father was wanting to voyage around the world,' he said sarcastically.

'She isn't. He isn't.'

'Then what the heck are you talking about? I think you must be touched. What do you mean? A handful of what?'

Why could he not understand?

'Listen,' I said desperately. 'I'm talking about the *jewels* from the *jewel* desks, the *jewel* desks we're sitting in now.'

'Jewel desks? Jewel desks?'

Then he tittered down the scale, in sudden delight. 'You mean *duel* desks.' He spelled the word – d-u-e-l. 'Duel desks. Duel meaning two, a fight with swords. Fighting a duel. A duel desk. Are some people dumb! You don't mean you really thought these were jewel desks with diamonds and rubies and precious stones?'

His disbelief was infectious; I began to wonder if I had believed it myself. Diamonds, rubies, sapphires, agate, moonstone, bloodstones?

'Not exactly,' I said, a traitor to my dreams. 'Not exactly.'

It did not seem fair that one word could promise so much, could have held so much power to organize and disorganize my life. How could I have been so at the mercy of one word? My betrayal by the word 'jewel' was a lasting blow dealt to me by the language I was encouraged to be at home in.

That night when I came home from school I opened our dictionary and by chance found both the words *duel* and *dual*. I read, dual: pertaining to two, shared by two, twofold, double; duel: a combat between two persons fought with deadly weapons by agreement, in the presence of witnesses.

It's *dual* desks, I thought, realizing that even my classmate, unknowingly was a victim of the treachery of the language. His interpretation of 'duel' desks might cause him more suffering than mine had. Duel desks. Duel. A combat fought by two people with deadly weapons by agreement, in the presence of witnesses. He could be preparing a catastrophe for himself.

I prized the information given to me by the dictionary, and the generous way it offered up its words to anyone who turned its pages. I had never before prized information though I knew others did, and I was familiar with its power to grant victory in many battles both with other children and with adults. I realize now that I did receive the jewels I had been promised. I had opened the dictionary and I had been showered with the inescapable words which, if I worked, could become my allies instead of my enemies.

20.

I have settled now in my flat.
I have arranged my favourite books on the bookshelf.
I have moved the table for working in privacy and light.

There's a ripe-grape-coloured cherry tree,
a bed of geraniums,
a woman walking in white shoes, white gloves, white hat.

A sea-gull circles the clock tower. His funereal white wings
recall pieces of old tombstone flying
when the wind strikes at the grave of a sea city.

Fog clouds drift on the hill.
Who lives, like an angel, in the clock tower?
The summer heat treads the colour from the cherry tree.
The gracious cultural burden of the View,
the long-faced clean houses that claim their natural right
to hold students, books, to have high ceilings, white walls, neat
flower beds,
will soon, I think, send my journeying memory into collapse.
Tomorrow I may be saying, There are no slums in St Kilda.
Hillside Road, the Workshops, Kensington are dreams.
I never lived in Playfair Street, Caversham, with my bedroom
a linen cupboard,
or waited on a Saturday night party at the Grand Hotel,
or tried to resist the pleas of my hangwomen workmates.
—You

need pearls.
Pearls take away that bare look from the neck.

Swans whose necks are bare
float on the Water of Leith.
The wind is south.
The century is late.

Six o'clock wine flows from the cherry tree.
Children go barefoot.
Men and women make promises.
None know, few care
who lives like an angel in the clock tower.

21.

With my rank growth and my proliferation of roots and a travel handbag of memories I returned to Baltimore toward the end of the northern winter. I had deceived myself into thinking that one or two deaths of relatives and friends may give immunity, at least for a few years, but even that year there was no immunity, and I see now how close death is to the process of 'going to seed,' for both are merely an abundance of life which shocks and frightens by its untidiness, its lack of boundaries and the finality of its choice of a place to grow.

Strangely enough, the ice pick and Mrs Tyndall came to mind now together, both as part of Brian's life and my work and the kind of pain that makes a writer want to throw away the words that are screens, moveable walls, decorations, unnecessary furniture, and keep only the load-bearing words (the load-bearing birds?) that stop the sky from falling.

First, the ice pick. It was kept at the top of the stairs near the barred window looking out over the alley. 'It's my only weapon,' Brian said.

I suspected he would never use it. He kept it as he kept the stained canvas rucksack of his young days, varnished and preserved within a frame on the wall, as a reminder of time spent in the southern Alps of New Zealand and of his first view of the Matukituki Valley. I have never seen the valley. It embodied Brian's dream of serenity and wild beauty, and it was partly his fear of losing the dream which made him keep the rusted ice pick with the broken handle. If he chose to keep a special memory, he embalmed an object rather than an image. His house was crowded with objects, many of them works of art, and others, like the ice pick and the rucksack and the hammer and plane that had belonged to his father, preserved as personal works of art, kinds of memories more reliable than the usual fading image, a retouched part of his life, guaranteed not to fade, yet also, like the ice pick, useful as a means of destruction in the cause of self-preservation. And at the time of my visit to Brian's house there was much talk of self-preservation, not in the sense of embalming, varnishing, but in surviving attack, for the city had one murder every day and many more robberies and muggings with violence both random and familial, and it was useless for a visitor to cry out, 'It's not my fault, I wasn't here in the beginning, I have no part in your city and your country's history, look at me, see how kind I am, how I smile, it's not my fault, see, I am different, I am a stranger.' Such pleas were self-evident lies, particularly in a city where the known poet died, and the responsibility of the truth brought gloom and hopelessness: I was not a stranger, I was there in the beginning, with the others.

In the general demand for weapons and seeing an advertisement in the local newspaper, and with example of the ice pick in mind, I bought from the bargain store down Monument Street, a tear gas *pen* in a small thin box, like the box for a fountain pen, the kind that used to be popular for presents at Christmas and on birthdays. I called myself a writer and this special pen had been advertised as one with special cartridges that could disable an attacker, perhaps cause momentary blindness, yet, because it was still 'only a pen' (it said so on the label, didn't it?) I bought it, and when I unwrapped it I was horrified to read the first sentence in the leaflet enclosed, Instructions for using your tear gas *gun*.

A simple mix-up of language. I ought to have known. The ice pick for use as blood-pick and past-pick. I can still hear my cry, 'But it's supposed to be a pen!'

I never used it. I put it away, guiltily, and when Mrs Tyndall, who came twice a week to clean the house, found it she knew at once what it was, she was horrified, knowing that pens are no longer refilled with ink, only with gas and explosives.

22.

Malfred knew that the family and the townspeople (who are always more shrewd than is to be admitted) were correct in naming her her father's daughter. She was her father's only child. Where Graham climbed mountains, Lucy knew the names of the native trees, but neither had made mountains or trees as separate dreams inside their mind, as Malfred had done. Malfred knew of the 'room two inches behind the eyes'; it was filled almost to overflowing; yet for forty years she had kept it locked. She had not planned that her exploration of it would be a dramatic occasion for herself or others. She kept remembering that when she was a child she had kept a fierce-looking beetle in a matchbox, not daring to look at it, and then when one day she found the courage to open the box, she found only a shrivelled, dry shell. But the shell had once been such a beautiful amber colour that having the beetle dead and gone did not seem important, for it had left behind the memory of its colour, of the shell that shone – yellow streaks on dark polished gold and amber. It had seemed incredible to Malfred that the thing, for so long unlooked at, had once been a creature, a pet with a name of its own. Howard. Yes, that was his name: Howard.

Malfred knew that she was on no human terms with the 'room two inches behind the eyes,' that what lay there, treasure or no treasure, did not belong to her, had not been captured by her and given a name. Perhaps it would never be captured and named. Yet she felt that for the first time in her life she was free to explore that room, and the fact that she was seizing the opportunity to explore branded her more surely than any other action had done as her father's daughter. What her father wanted to do, he had done, in time; he had been patient, persevering; his 'One day when I get the chance' had remained a genuine excuse, not the way of life it becomes for so many people, through their own deficiencies or through the sly workings of fate.

Malfred had been interested most of her life in painting. She was not sure that on Karemoana she would be inspired to paint; she wanted, first of all, to observe, to clean a dusty way of looking. From her collection of water colours she chose to take north with her, first, a painting of the mouth of the Waitaki in early winter; next, an old mill scene depicting the old mill at Matuatangi; then, a painting of the lonely headland where her father's statue had been set up. Other paintings she chose were a country scene on a day of a nor'wester, the old Main Street of Matuatangi with its wool and hide stores, early newspaper offices, rabbit-skin factory, new foundry. It was when she was trying to limit her choice of paintings that she realized (though she had known it for years, passively) how sentimental, colourless, were the images she had made of the scenes that were dearest to her; the true images were in her mind; she could stare at the mouth of the Waitaki in early winter without having to burden herself with a pile of dusty canvases that would remind her less of the scenes depicted than of the years spent 'teaching' art, pouncing on the faulty 'shadowers,' trying to instill the 'sense of proportion' that in her probationary years meant persuading schoolgirls to 'match' the sides of shovels and vases, to make distant mountains distant, near faces near; but which meant to her now an attempt to rearrange her own 'view,' set against the measuring standards not of the eye but of the 'room two inches behind the eyes.'

* * *

Now, with the upheaval of her journey north to her new life and her new way of seeing, Malfred had (or dreamed she had) emerged to see the long-treasured theories, once jewels, in their new, true form, as barnacles. Her shame at not having known pohutukawas was not as deep as it would have been in the 'old' days. Pohutukawas, geysers, Maori maidens – she knew none of these. Down south there had been few Maoris. She had learned about them at school – about the 'good' and the 'bad', the 'friendly,' the 'hostile'; all in a legend of the Fire in the Fern, Mr Busby, the cutting down of the Flagstaff. Lucy had a book of Maori fairy tales that Malfred had never been able to cope with, as she had with the Greek and Roman legends. Once or twice, in a burst of patriotism, she had asked the girls to illustrate a Maori legend – Rangi, Hinemoa, Maui. All except one girl – Lettice Bradley – had produced a painting that had no truth or conviction or foundation; as if the national history were too fragile to attract dreaming or the belief that follows dreaming. The same artificiality, Malfred knew, was evident in the printed book of fairy tales; it was clear that the illustrator had been thinking of Greece and Rome and not of AoteaRoa. Lettice Bradley, a gifted girl who, with Noni, could also draw the correct shadows of every object set before her, had made an unusual painting of Maui's fishing. She had lived and believed it. She 'knew' the legend, with the Biblical force of the word 'knew.'

Malfred remembered that she had not given Lettice the praise she deserved for her painting; and she remembered why: she had been awed by it, had been envious of it and of the secret store from which Lettice had drawn her knowledge and understanding of times that she had never experienced. Other pupils could paint certain scenes with reasonable skill – Paris in the Spring, Hercules and the Twelve Labours, Jason and the Golden Fleece – of these, Malfred had never felt envious, for the store of knowledge was common, the track to it was worn, repaired, signposted, as tourist tracks are, with the usual red and white picnic tables – mushroom-shaped, with matching stools – along the wayside. How had Lettice Bradley – Malfred said the name to herself now, as she lay in the dark – how had Lettice Bradley found her way to the secret store? Noni, her rival in shadows and fire shovels had never found this imaginative abundance.

Lettice Bradley. Lettice Bradley, come out here and be punished. Lettice Bradley, stay after school. . . Lettice Bradley who could never recite the terms of the Congress of Vienna or describe the Midland Railway network, or the importance of the Cheshire Salt Field or name the products of Birmingham – where had she visited in her dreams that she had been apprehended by the soul of her own country, like a calf branded early by the herdsman in whose paddocks it is born and by whose command it dies? Malfred had never been able to reconcile herself to Lettice Bradley's gift that showed itself in this special way only. Oh, it hadn't been fair, it still wasn't fair that an ordinary schoolgirl whose acknowledged favourite reading was Rudyard Kipling and Zane Grey had been able to absorb, as a mindless sponge absorbs food from the sea, the myths and legends of her own country; and yet to live, as an ordinary schoolgirl with her ordinary family in a rough-cast, flat-roofed bungalow that had a vegetable garden with tall, tied beans at the back and a square of lawn in front, to be mown on Saturday afternoons or Sunday mornings!

No, it wasn't fair, Malfred said to herself now. In the years since Lettice Bradley blossomed in her painting of Maui, Malfred had seen the envy that she had known, seem to become part of the national character. All up and down the country people began to beat their fists on walls, doors, mountains, on the boles of trees in the bush, even on the clouds and the moon and the stars in their (suddenly) 'own' sky, wanting to be let into the secret store, for the existence of it was no longer a secret. Someone, somewhere, had heard the rumour; the news was out; and it may have come to them, Malfred supposed – wiser now – from a source apparently more outlandish than Kipling and Zane Grey. It could have reached them through the Arabian Nights, or the Bible, or Shakespeare; or the current group of pop singers; or simply while they were staring at the garden spades and lawn fertilizer in the window of Woolworths. The news could have come through the waters of the Waitaki, it could have blown in the nor'wester – no one would ever know the source. But the news and the rumour of it had spread; it was part of daily life now to walk in the streets, stare at the people, and see the rumour in their eyes. The newspapers were full of it, and the beaches, the shops, the sports grounds; it was beaten out in the high, white boots of the marching girls; it was chanted in the pipes; it was boiled in the billy; and it rose from the lake with the seven-pound rainbow trout. It had flowed into the literature, the paintings; the country itself could not contain it; spontaneously, like a thistledown seed being carried by the wind as soon as it is ripe, it had spread 'overseas' where, instead of the formerly academic 'rumour' that, as official export had been subjected to such a lengthy quarantine that it had been forgotten or had died of the disease caught while it was being protected against the one it was feared to be suffering, it was now believed, it engendered new rumours that caused people to ask, turning their eyes to the Southern Hemisphere – Have you heard? Have you heard? They say . . . they say . . . Though such public asking does not often lead to the secret store, it may uncover new unsuspected treasures.

So one by one the items of national character became the centre of the rumour and of the new probe to get at the treasure. Putting kowhai, puarangi, manuka, rata, tarapunga on postage stamps and biscuit tins (the first stage was insertion in poetry), selling Maori carvings, faked or genuine, in Lower Queen Street where the overseas ships berth – all helped, or was thought to help; at least it took advantage of the knowledge that the rumour was about and that people were heeding it. And Malfred knew or sensed, smiling in sympathy with those who were so desperate to stake a claim in the identity of their country, that so many people were now trying to falsify genealogical tables so that they might be able to trace an obscure relative who was a Maori! They could just as well and happily have found that their great-great-grandfather was a boiling mud-pool or a piece of glacier or a spray of kowhai or pohutukawa blossom! Malfred was reminded, by this national claim for identity, of the phase that children experience when discovering that they are separate beings; they disown their parents and dream themselves into the exciting newness, individuality, uncertainty, of having been 'adopted.' Malfred realized that her envy of Lettice Bradley had concealed an envy of all who had 'known' – again in the Biblical sense; he *knew* her; she *knew* him – the myths and legends of the Maori, that is, an envy of the Maori who 'knew' the land. For a time, then, she had felt ashamed that none of her great-grandfathers were native chiefs or her grandmothers Maori princesses. She thought of the Maoris as she thought of Lettice Bradley. It wasn't fair that they should know so much, instinctively, about their country; that, when they looked at the sky, they might think, without self-consciousness, of Rangi, while Malfred's image seemed a poor secondhand one of Gods reclining on clouds, eating lotus and hurling thunderbolts. She had grown out of this naïve approach to myths, for myths, like rivers, come out of the common sea and return there, and none is alone; an Identi-Kit dream of *Wanted National Identity* may have the face of Hercules and the body of Maui; it may be just plain Mum and Dad . . . nor does it matter whether one's blood has been mixed with lava or pohutukawa blossom. . .

So I return to the pohutukawas, Malfred thought, these, and summer on Karemoana. And Wilfred . . . what was I thinking about Wilfred?

She gave a cry of surprise. She had been thinking that perhaps the prowler was Wilfred . . . returned from the dead. Her surprise was caused by her realizing that however hard he knocked at the door, and however long he stayed, she would never let him in.

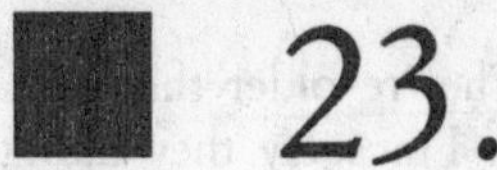

23.

Dear First Dad, remember you were the War? I remember that first winter away, how the woods were full of war and the snow made its own light, magnesium, mercury, splendour and flash in a sunless world. I saw the soldiers standing blind with the blood falling disguised as snow in the persuasion of purity. I looked again. They were pine trees. I inspected the withered limbs, the storm-blasted faces and bodies, all the seasoned carnage where sunlight, now and again on blue days, opened the wound of the scene showing – say – only a giant tree uprooted on its side, a half-headless hero drained of blood, his muscular convolutions of thought – chiefly his killing-pattern – exposed, his hope cramped in foetus shape. He wore a cap of icicles pointed and tasselled like a jester's, and his huge foot in its dead-leaf boot stuck in the sky. And no one came to bury the dead. Only the snow buried and uncovered, buried and uncovered, and the streams washed the bones, and the brown-and green-mottled army coats that others might have mistaken for dead leaves; and season after season the hummingbirds shuttled their patches of light across the eyeless faces.

* * *

The meal finished, those who could walk stood aside respectfully while the patients in the wheelchairs were taken to the lift. Following at the end of the procession, Tom avoided the small group of waiting wheelchairs and crutched up the stairway, and as he went along the corridor he heard weeping. Miriam was sitting crying in a chair in her ward. On the spare bed beside her, her new leg lay encased in its black lace-up shoe.

'They promised me a knee, they promised me a knee,' she said, looking up and seeing Tom.

Tom hobbled a little way into the room. He didn't know what to say. His mind was chiefly on 'the woman upstairs,' Ciss Everest, and the appalling possibility that it was *his* Ciss Everest.

'I had two daughters,' Tom said. 'They're older than you. They're grown up and away long ago. I'm sorry they didn't keep their promise about the knee.'

'They promised! Look at that shoe. It's like a Salvation Army foot. They said as soon as I was finished with the pylon I could have a real bending leg.'

She stopped crying. She pushed back her long brown hair, sniffed, wiped her nose, and looked curiously at Tom.

'What was wrong with you at lunch time?' she asked. 'You're not losing your leg are you?'

Tom tapped his white leg in its white pod.

'No. I'm keeping it.'

'You probably don't understand then.'

'Oh I do, I do!'

Peter had said that Miriam was a violinist. 'You've still got your music.'

Miriam made an exclamation of anger and impatience. 'Oh, it isn't *like* that! Why do you old people always play the game of adding and subtracting with remainders and so on, as if everything's equal to everything else, and if you lose something, well, you've something else left, as if it were all coins. Yes, I agree, I've still got my music. And this!'

She gestured towards the leg lying on the bed.

'There are others,' Tom said, 'worse off.'

'Oh I know, I know, but how does that help? It only makes it worse, it doesn't balance it, just because there are others. I'm an intelligent person, Mr Livingstone. I know that nothing balances like that. This is living, not keeping accounts. How does it help to know others are worse off? Look at poor Miss Everest.'

(The dead lying on violets and daisies like food on a decorated plate; a spring and summer dead more terrible than the winter dead in snow that is their shroud.)

'Is she very very sick?' Tom asked.

'Hopeless,' Miriam said abruptly. 'Are you feeling bad, Mr Livingstone? Is your leg hurting?'

'I'm tired. I believe they're making arrangements for me to fly home.'

'You're a long way from home. Where exactly do you live?'

'Waipori City. Quite a small place for a city. Our country leads the world in social legislation and experiment,' Tom said, suddenly aggressively proud of his distant country.

'Do you have anyone to visit you here?'

'No. I think I'll go to lie down.'

'Some can't rest. Peter is very brave.'

'He's in my ward. A nice kid.'

'His whole life is broken by this. Everyone here is seeing and experiencing revolution. Attack, assassination of the body followed by revolution and the new government.'

'Sounds too political for me.'

'It is,' Miriam said thoughtfully. 'It's the politics of helplessness.'

Tom said goodbye to Miriam and limped along the corridor. He passed two nurses.

'She can't be given it so soon.'

'The effect wears off. You know that.'

'But we must keep to the regular hours to give out medicine.'

'Miss Everest's in pain. You know what pain she's in.'

'We must think first of the smooth running of the whole ward. We're short of staff. We have to check every visit to the medicine cabinet and we simply can't unlock it every half-hour for one person only.'

Tom limped on past his ward to the women's four-bedded ward at the end of the corridor. He hesitated at the door and went in. Three of the beds were occupied by women resting clothed under the bedcovers while the fourth was screened from view by the usual rose-patterned screen that must have been a standard worldwide hospital design. Tom could hear the patient behind the screen whispering to the nurse.

An elderly woman, her neck, wrists, body set in a plaster splint, lay smiling, smiling, smiling. She saw Tom and directed her smile at him.

'You're the new patient? Having a look around? I'm Mrs Dockett.'

Smile, Smile. She wore glasses with black rims like the rims of the wheels of the wheelchairs. Her eyes gave the impression of spinning, spinning, spinning, their spokes whirling.

The nurse looked out from behind the screen.

'Mr I ivingstone, let the ladies rest. Go back to your ward.'

Tom listened. He felt sick and faint. The woman behind the screen was Ciss Everest, *his* Ciss Everest. He had thought of her for so many years with love and longing. He'd made her his shrine where his praise and his blame could be set, and time had so sanctioned for him the certainty of her perpetually remaining a shadow that her reappearance had the effect of toppling the pillars of love surrounding her and exposing their foundations of fear and hate and youthful uncertainty. He listened for her to cry out from behind the screen in her strong young voice: 'Livingstone, not Tom Livingstone?'

He heard no one calling his name. Rage came over him that a woman who had spread so wide in his world, for so many years that she had sucked up his life as the sun sucks up the sea and all the streams and rivers, should be lying so near him and yet make no sign to him. Unable to help himself he moved towards the screen and peered behind it as a surgeon, after making his incision, might peer in at the diseased place. He saw a frail golden-haired woman lying with her fist in her mouth and her mouth biting on it to suppress the cry of pain. She turned her eyes towards him. They were violet-coloured eyes, startling in her pale face, against her golden hair. She was Ciss Everest yet with a doll's hair in golden curls. She stared at him. She did not recognize him. She did not say: 'Tom, Tom Livingstone!'

Well he could throw away the photograph he'd kept for forty-five years, the one of him lying in the grass and her with the sunshade; and that other photograph taken at Stoke Poges. He'd protested at the idea of going there, saying that visiting graveyards was a morbid English custom. It was a bitter January day; he was a gloomy young man in his soldier's uniform, she a love-haunted young woman; the photograph, taken by the sexton in dim light, showed the snow-flattened battered grass, the grey putty-coloured tombstones, a colour of sickness, the locked budless trees with their branches like rods of iron. The scene was an aristocratic mockery of the vast European fields of putrid abominable death.

And when the sexton had gone, they sat together on the stone bench inside the porch, facing the weather-stained notices. They held hands. Tom remembered the sensation of the surrounding stone and the warm flesh hand. They kissed, scarcely a kiss, a light brushing of the lips and thistledown breaths, surrounded by the dead who, should they waken from beneath their stone, would breathe heavily and greedily.

Well he could throw away all those cherished memories, with the photograph, for he now possessed the image of an old tart with dyed hair, a life-sized doll mechanized to cry out in pain every few minutes, to groan in the night, to whisper her pleas for morphine. The Ciss Everest Cancer Doll. This way to see the Ciss Everest Cancer Doll. Real hair that can be washed, dried, combed, permed. Real face that can be made up to hide the age and the tears. This way, this way to the Ciss Everest Cancer Doll, Doll of the Years, Doll of Forty-Five Years, This way to Miss World War I!

Tom huddled, suddenly in pain. A fever speckled his forehead, like something crawling over his skin. He cried out and a nurse came to help him.

'You've no right to be wandering in the women's ward like this.' She fetched a wheelchair, helped him into it, and wheeled him to his room.

'On to your bed at once to rest, Mr Livingstone.'

* * *

Tom dozed again, waking at suppertime when he eased himself from his bed, peglegged to the washstand and splashed his face with cold water. A low fever still burned on his skin. Peter was already downstairs watching television while he waited for the supper gong. It sounded, as from deep in a well, like a summons. There was the grinding movement of wheelchairs being hurried to the landing, then the swift footsteps like those of someone who naturally flew but who, out of discretion and sympathy, now chose to walk. Those steps were always those of the staff, as no patient walked easily, for although all were not crippled, each learned to deflect possible envy and to make himself acceptable and in harmony with his surroundings by acquiring a token limp or an awkwardness and slowness of movement. Firm healthy walking was not recommended.

A nurse passing Tom's ward looked in.

'Suppertime, Mr Livingstone. You're having supper in Miss Everest's ward?'

No, no, no.

'Yes,' Tom said.

He moved slowly to the ward and opened the door. Dressed and blanketed, Miss Everest sat in a deep armchair near the window overlooking the front garden. Tom hobbled over and sat in a chair opposite her, with the supper table, already set, between them. He stared at her, coldly, curiously, trying to read the past in her face, to extract it like some kind of invisible writing beneath his glance. He thought of Eleanor, eaten, early in their marriage, by the two children who swung from her breasts like little monkeys dangling from the buds of a tree; and then eaten by his own impatience and coldness and his longing for another woman.

He watched Ciss Everest's face. She did not recognize him. He saw that the clear violet eyes had grown an opaque film, like pondweed. She must be seventy now, he thought. She was an old woman and he was an old man. And as he stared at her she became an old woman he had never known, and he almost believed that her name and the repeating of it by the patients and the nurses and his own mind was a trick he was playing upon himself, for when he glanced away from her and turned quickly back, almost before he himself realized it, she resembled his own daughter Naomi, she *was* Naomi. Now how could that have been? And then once again she became the Ciss Everest with whom out of politeness and sympathy he had agreed to share a meal, eating, munching, knifing, forking, scraping, saying ah ah, oh oh, yes yes yes, and smiling, smiling, smiling, for he too was learning the politics of helplessness.

'Good evening Mr Livingstone.'

He started.

So she did recognize him. He stared harder at her face. He

remembered his passion and haunting, the pain and delight her memory had caused him. But where had his memory gone? Where had the time gone? There was so little room in his mind in which to keep what remained. He had tried to preserve it all so painstakingly – indeed, in 'taking pains' he had been forced to endure them and distribute them among his bewildered family.

But she had gone from him now. Nothing stayed. Only his childhood stayed. And the War? The older he became the more his childhood years became clear to him, seen in a new light manufactured by the accumulation of years and switched on, full voltage, day and night by the luxurious necessity of approaching death. A room with no corners shadowed. A room where, because one had not yet learned to read, one imagined the many warning notices were entertaining pictures. Tom had had ten brothers and two sisters, like a family in a fairy tale, the tale where someone was always missed out when treasures such as wings were being distributed. All the brothers and sisters were dead now except Leonard, the black sheep, the drunkard.

'Good evening, Miss Everest. Have you had a good day?'

(He had learned the ritual. In the morning: Have you had a good night? In the evening: Have you had a good day?)

Miss Everest smiled a floating smile.

'Not bad at all. A bit niggly. Yes, definitely niggly at times.'

The nurse brought two plates of scrambled eggs and toast and tea, bread and butter and raspberry jam, and two pieces of chocolate cake with chocolate icing half an inch thick.

Tom rebelled against being classified as a 'scrambled egg' patient. If he had been dining downstairs he would have been eating beans or sausages or curried stew, indelicate dishes that gave one the illusion of being in stout health.

'And have you had a good day Mr Livingstone?'

He answered abruptly.

'My leg's mending. Plaster comes off tomorrow.'

He wondered what she would say if he asked: 'Do you remember, Ciss, that time in London when I first met you? I was a wounded soldier and you gave me special care and you let me keep my gas mask and sleep with it under my pillow, because

I could not bear to part with it. I never did part with it, Ciss. I took it home with me to Waipori City and I've had it with me all my life. I showed it to my wife and two daughters, by God I showed it to them, and it scared them all but it didn't scare you, Ciss Everest.'

But Miss Cecily Everest, floating on the ebbing tide of her morphine, wanted only to chatter.

'I've been ill a long time you know. It started years ago. I used to be a nurse, so I know something about it. And now at last they've broken the news to me. They've broken it to me gently.'

She waited, perhaps for him to ask what they had broken to her, but he said nothing.

'The news of course,' she said impatiently as if he had questioned her. 'The news that I shan't recover; they're sending me to a nursing home not far away – that's why I'm here in the first place, waiting for a bed.'

She leaned forward. Her face was flushed.

'It's not far from here. This is a Recovery Unit, you know. I can't stay here. Promise to visit me when I go to the nursing home to die. Promise!'

The demand startled Tom. Perhaps she had recognized him after all?

'I'm sure you'll have many visitors,' he said soothingly.

'Promise.'

'Of course.'

'I like having supper with you here. It's like being at home. I never had a home of my own. I've just lived in hospitals as a nurse and then as a patient. I never married. This is like our home, isn't it, just us two sitting here eating our supper.'

Tom played the game.

'It is indeed.'

'I used to go down to the noisy dining room, but now I just sit here. They dress me for supper on most evenings. It's quiet up here, just us two, like around the fire at home. I can pretend I've invited you to supper.'

'Yes, yes.'

They finished their meal. Tom had a horrifying glimpse of

Ciss Everest in the reality of her hideous long blonde hair. Meet Ciss Everest, Miss War of Nineteen-Seventeen, the World's only cancer doll, Doll of the Year, Doll of Forty-five Years, Doll of the Future.

The next moment he had the privacy of his nightmare ripped open with a brutality that he had often practised himself but could not forgive in others. Leaning forward suddenly, Ciss Everest raised her hands to her head and removed her long golden wig, exposing her bald head.

'See,' she said. 'I wear a transformation.'

Hearing her say it in her slow dreamily deliberate way, callously as if she were trying to convey some fearful message to him, he felt himself growing dizzy, his heart beating heavily with a turn-over gurgling of blood around it. She had recognized him, surely!

'Since the radiation made me bald I've worn this transformation.'

He'd never heard a wig called by that name before. The word horrified him in its exactness of meaning and description. He felt that if she repeated it with such mocking deliberation he would jerk his hand forward and slap her face.

Then he began to cry. He sobbed. His shoulders sagged as if they were made of straw, suddenly buffeted, the prop removed.

'Nurse,' Miss Everest called. 'Nurse.'

She pressed the bell by her bed.

A nurse came at once into the room.

'Nurse, this old man's crying.'

'Now now Mr Livingstone, we can't have that, and you with only a broken leg while here's our Miss Everest so ill, and you're upsetting her.'

The nurse turned, speaking gently to Miss Everest. 'Would you like to go to bed now?'

Miss Everest raised shining, craving eyes to the nurse. 'I'll have the injection now,' she whispered. 'I'll have the injection.'

The nurse led Tom from the room. 'An old man like you!' she exclaimed.

He felt too tired and sick to protest that he was not an old man, he was only eighteen, a young soldier wounded in the

War. He'd seen more blood and sickness and death than this Recovery Unit would know in a hundred years; and he was only eighteen, too young to kill and be killed. He had a right to cry, a right to scream if he wanted to, with rage and unhappiness.

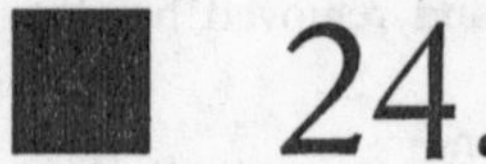

24.

It was midnight when Mattina was awakened by the cries. She sat up in bed, alarmed, listening to the chorus of screams, shrieks, wailings from Kowhai Street: a clamour such as she had not heard since the days of the riots in Park Avenue when thousands raging for freedom and equality of opportunity, attacked the department stores and carried away goods, clothing, appliances, books, records, leather jackets in particular; a riot of have-not trying to transfer identity by acquiring a mass of goods that clicked, spoke, opened, shut, played, cooked, heated, cooled, switched on and off, transformed, gave pictures, sounds, voices; and warmed, warmed.

In Kowhai Street the rage of cries continued without decrease, seeming to come from every home, and as Mattina listened, shivering in the chill of midnight, fear quelled her first impulse to investigate the fury. She tried to stay calm. She regretted she had not taken the flight home weeks ago after one day in Kowhai Street and the news of the murder of the penultimate Madge, for it seemed to her now that her life had grown increasingly strange in its shifting dimensions, and if she were to believe Dinny Wheatstone, the imposter novelist, the Gravity Star was exerting its influence, bearing its overwhelming unacceptable fund of new knowledge from millions of light-years and centuries of springtime. Mattina was aware suddenly that the breathing presence had gone from her room leaving a ragged spear of abandoned light dizzying around the room as the wake or wash of – the vanished star? An animal star? An illogical unknowing unformed star? It was crazy, an invasion of madness with all the classic symptoms appearing in the overthrown space. Had the Gravity Star or the implications of its existence seized Kowhai Street, and would it later seize Puamahara, allying itself to the first source, the Memory Flower containing the land memory, to begin its work of transforming being, thought, language?

If I were writing this story, Mattina thought, the words might have begun already to burn, and though still legible they would sink into the flames as if they desired their own oblivion.

Mattina wondered, do the people of Kowhai Street know of the demolition of their minds and their words – is that why they rage without ceasing?

She was calm now. She felt within herself a cleanness, an emptiness as if her mind and heart had become dark empty rooms disconnected from light with no switch to banish darkness. She groped her way, as if she were blind, to the bedroom door and out into the hall; opening the front door, she felt again the force of the cries and screams. She walked down the path to the grass verge on the street. The families of Kowhai Street stood at their gates or in their driveway, screaming and shrieking; the children too. Hercus Millow's two cats stood by his side howling with an unearthly note of searching and despair. The Shannons were calling as if from southern to northern mountain. The Hanueres made a plaintive lament. The Jameses were sobbing, the Townsends cried and shrieked. Only Dinny Wheatstone and Mattina were silent. And although the empty homes of Madge McMurtrie and George Coker had no one at their gates, from each house came a succession of horrifying human cries as if from someone trapped within the walls.

Listening, Mattina realised that no part of the chorus had words of any recognizable language. The sounds were primitive, like the first cries of those who had never known or spoken words but whose urgency to communicate becomes a mixture of isolated syllables, vowels, consonants; yet within and beyond the chorus, recognizable as long as the human brain held some stem (of crystal, bone, iron, stone, gossamer), there came a hint, an inkling of order, a small strain recognizable as music, not a replacement of what had been lost but a new music, each note effortlessly linking with the next, like dew-drops or mercury after momentary separation from the whole; yet 'momentary', now, was centuries old, and even the midnight roses along the path to Mattina's mailbox were roses of an Ancient Springtime.

It was not entirely the cries that brought a renewed feeling of horror: it was the faces, the bodies, the clothes of the people of Kowhai Street. Mattina, feeling she had *known, invested in* each family, observed in the glare of the street lights, Hercus Millow, the Shannons, the Jameses, the Townsends, the Hanueres, all changed beyond belief. The surface of the road, the footpath, the lawns and front gardens had all changed. Everyone's clothes appeared to be in shreds as if each person had been attacked. Both day and night clothes were smeared with a mixture resembling clay, mud, with bright specks and clusters like sequins or diamonds that were also scattered over the road, the front lawns and gardens, and even on the walls and roofs of the houses. The people did not move from where they stood while they continued to scream. Their eyes were bright like animal eyes seen in the dark, small electric bulbs glowing the length of the street. Not daring to move at first, but aware that the changes had not overtaken her, her house and garden, Mattina, trembling, struggling against an increasing numbness in her legs and her arms, forcing her to cling to the mailbox for support, found herself staring directly into Hercus Millow's face; for though he stood several yards away, there was an apparent failure of the concept of distance to become reality, and Mattina found herself reading his face as she might read a telegram held close to her. His rage mixed with confusion; he showed a grief as at a loss so sudden and dreadful that neither he nor any of his neighbours had been able to predict its nature or prevent it. His face was a changing mask of hopelessness.

No longer able to bear his glance, Mattina looked up at the sky. She thought, surprised at such a natural event, 'Why, it's raining.' Yet the falling rain was not 'real' rain. Specks, some small as carrot seed (George Coker had shown her his packets of garden seed), others as large, mapped purple and grey, as beanseed, some like hundreds-and-thousands, other like dew-drops set with polished diamonds, rubies, emeralds; or plain dew-drops that flowed in changing shapes among the layers of seeds and seed-pearls and jewels white and brown and red pellets of clay and then earth-coloured flecks of mould; smears of dung, animal and human, and every 'raindrop' and mixture of jewels and waste, in shapes of the 'old' punctuation and language – apostrophes, notes of music, letters of the alphabets of all languages. The rain was at once alive in its falling and flowing; and dead, for it was voiceless, completely without sound. The only sound was the continuing rage from the people of Kowhai Street.

Gradually controlling her panic, her surprise that the rest of Puamahara seemed to be sleeping peacefully enough, that the highways bordering Kowhai Street were, as usual, slightly less busy and noisy than during the day (their sound was strangely unrelated to the sound and quiet of Kowhai Street), Mattina returned to the house and protecting herself with the overshoes at the back porch, she found the courage to walk across the road to Hercus Millow who, seeing her, stopped screaming and stared, his lamp-eyes glistening and glowing. The two cats stopped their wailing, and making small meows, sank low and crept towards the house as if stalking unseen prey. Their fur was coated with the new kind of rain, now with a scab of dung, now with a cluster of jewels, yet they did not lick obsessively or paw at their coats.

Mattina stood hoping that Hercus Millow might speak. Although his lips moved and his throat and tongue worked in an attempt at speech, the sounds he made were grunt, moan and, finally, scream. In the end he gave up trying as had the others in Kowhai Street. Having found their new voice, they accepted it and soon began to control it. They no longer screamed although some, out of fury and despair or helplessness, still made intermittent animal-like cries.

'What is it?' Mattina asked, pronouncing her words carefully in a luxury of untroubled speech and aware of the suffering in the eyes of the listening Hercus.

'What has happened in Kowhai Street?'

Hercus stared, whimpering in what she took to be an attempt

to answer her until she realized that although he had appeared to be listening, he had understood none of her words. They were foreign to him. What had happened, what would happen, what should she do? And how would the other residents of Puamahara react when they discovered the plight of Kowhai Street?

She could now see Dinny Wheatstone, apparently normal in her imposture, leaning over her gate, watching and listening. And the Townsends, they too were muttering a new speech, their night clothes in shreds, covered with the new kind of rain. Perhaps, Mattina thought, because I'm from another country and Dinny Wheatstone is a crazy imposter, we have been spared transformation within Puamahara, this night as the Gravity Star shines beside the Memory Flower.

Then even as Mattina watched, one by one the residents of Kowhai Street, silent now, returned inside their homes, and after another glance up and down the street, at the roadway glittering with its newly fallen rain, Mattina went inside to her sitting room and sat at the table and drawing aside the curtain, looked out at the darkened shapes of the trees. She could see the halo of morning light on the farthest peaks of the mountains, as if beyond the peaks there were another world with another morning and promise of a day that bore no relation to Kowhai Street.

Leaning back in her chair, Mattina gripped the edge of the table as if to steady herself in the shock of an earthquake. Then she began to sob, without having spare breath, so that her indrawn breaths became groans; she rocked to and fro. Was this how it would be? Was this how any disaster would be, how she would behave when it happened? In a country of earthquakes there was constant talk of disaster, with the earthquakes, the volcanic eruptions, being used to mask other disasters more feared, perhaps more expected. Mattina had found that Kowhai Street talked often of First Aid, that most of the residents had their Safety Bucket containing medicines, candles, matches, materials for shelter and warmth, their solar-powered radio, tinned food; and so on; but what use now was a plastic blanket and a tin of Irish stew? And what was the nature of the disaster?

Mattina switched on her radio to the local station, the talkback show. Perhaps they would advise her, they would announce the disaster in Kowhai Street.

The same old talkback show: beat them, whip them, hang them, put them on an offshore island out of sight, they're cheating us, they're bludgers, love is what the world needs, more and more love; and castrate them.

No news of Kowhai Street. Mattina switched off the radio. Her sobbing over, her arms no longer gripping the table, she laid her hand on the tablecloth. She noticed a small cluster like a healed sore on the back of her left hand. She picked at it. The scab crumbled between her fingers and fell on the table into a heap the size of a twenty-cent coin. Examining it, she discovered it to be a pile of minute letters of the alphabet, some forming minute words, some as punctuation marks; and not all were English letters – there were Arabic, Russian, Chinese and Greek symbols. There must have been over a hundred in that small space, each smaller than a speck of dust yet strangely visible as if mountain-high, in many colours and no colours, sparkling, without fire. It could not be possible that the bones of the world's written and spoken languages, at the onset of their destruction, had fallen first on Kowhai Street, Puamahara; that the residents of Kowhai Street, under the influence of the Gravity Star and the legend of the Memory Flower had each suffered a loss of all the words they had ever known, all the concepts that supported and charged the words, all the processes of thinking and feeling that once lived within the now shattered world of their words. The people of Kowhai Street had experienced the disaster of unbeing, unknowing, that accompanies death and is thought by man to mark the beginning of a new kind of being and thought and language that, in life, is inconceivable, unknowable. The people of Kowhai Street, still alive, were now unintelligible creatures with all the spoken and written language of the world fallen as rain about them. The only judgment likely to be made about them, should their plight be discovered, was a diagnosis of mass hysteria or insanity. They were alive, yet on the other side of the barrier of knowing and being. There might be those who would judge them as better dead, who might even wish to induce a 'merciful' death.

Mattina wondered what might happen if by morning all the world's words had fallen upon every corner of the world, if everyone had been transformed to a similar state of unbeing and unknowing, if a universal process of new knowing, new thinking and feeling, and a new language might then fall, transforming life on earth to a new stage, unknowable yet, until the influence of the discovery of the Gravity Star had touched first one, then another, then many areas of the earth most receptive at that moment to geological and spiritual explosions and earthquakes. Whatever happened in Puamahara, if it were an intimation of the future, built on the memory of the past, a memory treasured enough to be thought of as a precious flower, a fountain flower at the gate of the orchard of the Housekeepers of Ancient Springtime, or if it were merely a dream, the town would surely learn as other other towns have done, to accept and profit from its new myth. Hamelin town in Brunswick, Lourdes, Jonestown in Guyana. No town could be immune to the planting of new myths and legends, for were not these the few ways in which human beings may live, without disaster, in both the known and unknown worlds? That is, until now, and the arrival of the knowledge of the Gravity Star. Or could the Gravity Star be simply a modern myth?

Mattina sat for two hours looking out at the back garden, the one or two cat-shapes appearing and disappearing in the grass; a heavily winged morepork flying slowly from the tall puriri at the end of the garden. She could still hear murmurs and cries from Kowhai Street; they were muted now like the sound of the wind, as if they had always been.

Then, at four o'clock, feeling too exhausted to know or think or feel or plan, Mattina returned to her bed. She did not ask again why the breathing presence had disappeared. She lay down, closed her eyes, and slept.

And woke. And it was morning.

PART THREE

reflections

A writer must go alone through the gateway entered or arrived at, out into the other 'world' with no luggage but memory, and a pocketful of words, some of which may be like shells crumbled to sand before the oncoming waves, while others may turn out to be jewels – turquoises – that time has shown to be the teeth of the dead mastodons.

('Memory', p. 487)

And how long could the people of the world survive, walking through the ashes of their languages, having little clue now to their thoughts and feelings, not knowing how to bring new languages to birth?

(*Carpathians*, pp. 116–17)

■ 25.

I'm never going to write another story.

I don't like writing stories. I don't like putting he said she said he did she did, and telling about people, the small dark woman who coughs into a silk handkerchief and says excuse me would you like another soda cracker Mary, and the men with grease all over their clothes and lunch tins in their hands, the Hillside men who get into the tram at four forty five, and hang on to the straps so the ladies can sit down comfortably, and stare out of the window and you never know what they're thinking, perhaps about their sons in Standard two, who are going to work at Hillside when it's time for them to leave school, and that's called work and earning a living, well I'm not going to write any more stories like that. I'm not going to write about the snow and the curly chrysanthemums peeping out of the snow and the women saying how lovely every cloud has a silver lining, and I'm not going to write about my grandmother sitting in a black dress at the back door and having her photo taken with Dad because he loved her best and Uncle Charlie broke her heart because he drank beer. I'm never going to write another story after this one. This is my last story.

I'm not going to write about the woman upstairs and the little girl who bangs her head against the wall and can't talk yet though she's five you would think she'd have started by now, and I'm not going to write about Harry who's got a copy of We were the Rats under his pillow and I suppose that's called experience of Life.

And about George Street and Princes Street and the trams up to twelve. I'm not going to write about my family and the house where I live when I'm in Oamaru, the queerest little house I've ever seen, with trees all round it oaks and willows and silver birches and apple trees that are like a fairy tale in October, and ducks waggling their legs in the air, and swamp hens in evening dress, navy blue with red at the neck, nice and boogie-woogie, and cats that have kittens without being ethical.

And my sister who's in the sixth form at school and talks about a Brave New World and Aldous Huxley and DH Lawrence, and asks me is it love it must be love because when we were standing on the bridge he said. He said, she said, I'm not going to write any more stories about that. I'm not going to write any more about the rest of my family, my other sister who teaches and doesn't like teaching though why on earth if you don't like it they say.

That's Isabel, and when it's raining hard outside and I think of forty days and forty nights and an ark being built, when it's dark outside and the rain is tangled up in the trees, Isabel comes up to me, and her eyes are so sad what about the fowls, the fowls I can see them with their feathers dripping wet and perches are such cold places to sleep. My sister has a heart of gold, that's how they express things like that.

Well I'm not going to do any more expressing.

This is my last story.

And I'm going to put three dots with my typewriter, impressively, and then I'm going to begin . . .

I think I must be frozen inside with no heart to speak of. I think I've got the wrong way of looking at Life.

26.

Country stuff, not too much sweetness, not too much tooth and claw; mix the dead toads discreetly with the crushed lilac; a single toil and trouble laced with blackberry and balm; don't forget the broiler houses (cross between mortuaries and school gymnasiums). But then you're writing it, get on with it.

Unity Foreman smiled, considering the editor's letter.

The Charming Village of Little Burgelstatham.

Letter from the Countryside.

Dear Reader.
The distant and near fields do look green
with wheat and summer perfection of trees, the peacetime mapping
of cloud reveals no sinister shape, the wild creatures run free,
the ditches and ponds are deep where swimming things may
  swim—
surely nothing is drowned, face-downwards,
turning in violence from the Olde English dream?
Conservative ladies pursue their habits of roses, honeysuckle,
blackberries, display wild sweet peas and pink may,
bridal nettle, muscle-bursting hogweed, Mr Universe of
  the hedges . . .
Is there place for the dying toad, like a lump of wound
  lava? spurt of blood,
the adder, grinning rat, deadly nightshade?

'Oh,' Unity said, kissing out with crosses what she had written, and beginning again.

In this peaceful rural Suffolk village where I've come to describe to readers the kind of life lived today in the countryside of England, the window of my thatched cottage looks out upon a ripening field of wheat, upon hedges of roses and honeysuckle, blackberries in blossom, tall grasses that glitter in the early-morning dew. But what of the people who still pursue this pleasantly rural way of life untouched by the turmoil of city pressures? Now, as I look from my window, I see—

a bus ticket coming over the wall. That's the third thrown over this past ten minutes. Why do I have to live in a flat so near a bus-stop?

A jet screamed overhead. The harsh June traffic, which, in winter fog and snow, had been reduced to a restrained felt-pedalled murmur, ran riot with noise under the high sky extravagant with summer light. Unity went to the window and shut it. The room was stuffy, full of carpet dust and invading soot. She reopened the window, in time to see another bus ticket drifting over the garden wall.

'Hell,' she said. 'Hell.'

She returned to her typewriter.

> Here, in the peaceful village of Little Burgelstatham, where I've rented this country cottage for the summer, life pursues its peaceful way. At the same time modern progress has made way for subtle changes not always appreciated or understood by the inhabitants. The poultry farms are an example. Only yesterday I was invited to inspect a broiler house. Not without some trepidation I entered and saw—

the Piccadilly crowds at rush-hour travelling up and down the escalators feasting their eyes on little X-tras and Living Bras.

God, what a life.

Unity realized suddenly that she was tired, and leaning on her typewriter, she dozed a few minutes. When she woke there were marks on her forehead, for she had removed the typewriter cover: bbbbb,,,787654££££; the ££££££££ marks were prominent.

She quickly finished her 'Letter from the Countryside,' posted it to Cornstalk, and relaxed in a hot bath.

Oh there were empty houses and houses half-constructed where, as children, we stamped about on the bare winter-pale wood sending up a cloud of sawdust into the half-formed rooms, where the wall-frames rose up like thin unfleshed arms and the roof was partly sky, summer-blue, endless as our vision of childhood and life without death. There were houses surrounded by trees and houses without trees, and houses within trees; with swamps and red-weeded ponds and lank grasses crowned and veiled by the eternal spider-houses with their tenuous, swinging, sparkling stairways leading from door to door across the air; for the spiders and the beetles and the birds also looked for shelter and hiding-place; and even the blood in our bodies had its own secret cell where the structure of its life could be cherished in health and preyed upon, destroyed, in sickness; and whatever happened to the blood-cell happened also to the houses, in a different form with a different name – in the strewn beetle legs and the stray bird feather and in the spilled blood, seen or unseen, in the curtained human house.

All night I dreamed of those houses – the early places by the railway line, by the railway goodshed or the engine shed, the tall macrocarpas, the piled sacks of grain with their stuffy dusty smell, the railway colour of the paint on the railway huts, the trucks, the sheds, the house roofs; and all the other houses, unrailway, with yellow banksia roses and a deep yellowed bath and big high-ceilinged rooms with the piles of borer-dust along the floor by the skirting boards and in the corners and behind the door and the mirrored wardrobe; and then the formal houses, those of other people, full of fear and strangeness and foreign order, with hostile other-smelling furniture and level undented beds and crocheted doilies and fringed blinds; and lace; and china, blue china cups and saucers that let in a faint blue light which shone on the faces of the adult tea-drinkers, the aunts, cousins, neighbours, giving their skin a blue sheen, like celluloid: artificial, inflammable; with eyes chipped, in glass moulds; the terrible strangers in the best-behaviour holiday houses stacked and stocked with *pleases* and *thank yous* with a small heap of *may I's* and *pardon me's* packed among the few layers of threadbare hand-me-downs in the holiday suitcase, the family suitcase lined with a silk that was called 'shot' silk – grey, streaked with its own blood.

I dreamed of my first formal house, my foreign cushioned carpeted bed-sitting room in the home of Mrs Tomlin in Maori Hill, Dunedin; Mrs Tomlin who each year 'took in' a student boarder and whose life was overflowing with her married daughter and her grandchildren, and who spent most of her time with them in the new government estate over the hill. Lorna and Tom and the children. She never tired of talking about them. She'd be up early in the morning with her coat and hat on, ready to go 'over the hill' to Lorna's place, and every evening at the dinner table that was always crowded with plates and little dishes and china boats and bowls, with mounds of moist food streaming like small volcanoes, she'd talk of the day at Lorna's, a detailed account from moment to moment.

My room was dark with a polished floor and a window so modestly and carefully dressed that a glimpse of light rarely showed except when I cautiously sprang the brown fringed blind up a few inches. Once or twice when it rushed up the full length of the window, a rectangular block of light came hurtling in, striking the dressing table and the carpet and the polished floor and the bed and the slippery rose coloured bedspread with a blow that threatened to rob them of all colour in the sun-suffering process known as 'fading.' Then I hastily retrieved the blindcord and shut out the sun.

'Keep the curtains drawn and the blinds down; it's the only defence,' Mrs Tomlin said. 'I've seen some shocking examples of fading.'

Her one complaint about Lorna was that she allowed all her furnishings to fade.

'And I trained her so well!'

I dreamed, too, of the hospital cells with the small high-up, barred and shuttered window, and the door that had no inside handle, and I recalled my feeling of horror each time I touched the door and found nothing to grasp. Have you ever lived in a room where the door has no handle on the inside, where the bed is a straw mattress on the floor, the blanket a square of grey canvas, and the chamber pot a stinking licorice-black rubber vessel, grey at the rim where the urine has aged it, where the walls are stained and scarred, where they have been beaten and thumped and kicked by frightened people? They had left their fossilized screams and cries, like a mine, for me to explore, and in one corner, though you could not see it unless you found the right focus, there was a mountain of salt formed through the many seasons of many tears, and all over the walls and ceiling and the floor, the oval shape of the peephole-peeping eyes had burned their brand. Those cells were cells of despair. They were the last place to be: after that, there was nowhere; they were the rehearsals of death while the thousand eyes were the steady uncaring eyes of grass blades and sun-filled daisies and marigolds, the burr marigolds, the tickseed sunflowers that leave the stain of their touch only on the living. Made warm by them, what do the living care about death? After all, the sun returns each day to the sky, the promise of morning is kept, in spite of cathedral arguments, the stony-faced insistences about the identity of the originator of the promise.

You see, I was carried away in my dream, as one may be. And I dreamed of other dwelling-places, in my first journey away from New Zealand after Lewis died and I travelled through the Spanish islands and knew the earth and flowers and creatures that surround the houses: that snow-smelling bedroom in the Pyrenees with the big featherbed; and the slices of snow wedged in the window; the almond and beanflower-smelling rooms in the islands where the windows overlook the sea and the sand, and the dry homeless tumbleweed roams across the beach, curled upon itself, blown over and over in the wind; and the salt marshes burn with blue flowers.

And I dreamed of the house on the island in the Bahamas with the furry rats on my pillow, and the scorpions on the floor and the diamond-backed rattle of the coconut palms in the night wind; of the marigold-smelling Flint Cottages of Norfolk; and the cabbage- and varnish-smelling bedsitter in London where my daughter Edith lived until she found her flat; the soot-smelling rooms that were 'home,' the plastic slop and water buckets, the whistling kettles, the gas rings with the gas lingering at every joint, crevice, around the gas pipe, beneath the window-sill, and in the tenants too, in their joints and crevices, at their fingertips, on their skin, while their hearts must have surrendered their power of beating to the city traffic which, like a giant pacemaker, took over heart-duty, while the actual heart remained in its role of a tired bedsitter muscle, kin at last with the metal gas ring, the frayed linen, the thread-bleeding carpet and the chipped cold-water sink on the landing.

I dreamed of all the houses and homes and nests of the world's real and unreal estate; the originals, the replicas; and even of the wheelbarrow home which I saw in the shelter of a London bank, closed for the weekend, with an old woman and her four cats and two dogs and her bundle of possessions, setting up house for the weekend, the animals without murmur or bark, still as corpses in the wheelbarrow while the old woman, her coat spread beneath her, an old blanket over her, her head pillowed on the bundle of clothing, slept in the sheltered entrance to the bank beneath the poster which said, 'Your financial problems solved. Instant housing loans. No fuss no waiting personal attention.' The old woman slept, her arm around one of the cats, a mottled grey mangy creature with a bitten left ear and a purr that, rivalling the shudder of the underground trains, nearly shook the foundations of neighbouring Kings Cross, St Pancras, and Euston Stations.

And I thought of the room in Menton in the villa where Margaret Rose Hurndell had lived, and how I had visited the room. I walked up a narrow street beneath a railway bridge and up another street that had once been a Roman road, and on the left I saw the plaque, *Margaret Rose Hurndell Memorial Room*, giving the date of her birth and death (born 1930 – the same year as the Princess Margaret Rose – died in 1957; and like Peter Wallstead largely unknown until after her death) and a list of her writings. The garden was overgrown with weeds, the stairs leading to the small garden were thick with sodden leaves and fragments of paper thrown off the street. I put the Margaret Rose Hurndell Key (which I had borrowed) in the lock and pushed open the sun-blistered wooden door which permitted itself to open halfway: it had 'dropped' like an old used womb. I walked in. I opened the tiny windows, pushing back the branches that crowded against them. The room slowly became 'aired' like old stored linen. Small chutchutting birds with whistlings and secretive noises began stirring outside. A cool wind blew through the windows and out the door, a between-winter-and-spring wind. There was an air of desolation in the room and beyond it. A water-spotted plaque inside gave further details of Margaret Rose Hurndell's career. There were a few straight-backed vicarage-type chairs in the room, and a desk and a bookshelf (an Armstrong Fellow came each year to work in the memorial room); and layers of cold along the bare, tiled floor. I could hear the grass swaying in the neglected garden, and the brittle rustling of the flax bush, now a mass of soaring green spears, which a sympathetic writer had planted near the crumbling wall.

Here, I thought, if one were a spirit or dead, is a sanctuary. With a sudden rush of wind, dead leaves, twigs and a scrap of paper blew inside. The air of desolation and neglect increased: the chill, of the wind and of the spirit, intensified and there was the kind of peace that one feels walking among the dead and listening, as the dead may, at a great distance from the world and its movement and noise.

I went to explore the small garden and found a green garden seat which I cleared, brushing away the bruised ripe loquats fallen everywhere from the huge loquat tree; and I lay down, half in the sun, half in shadow, looking up at the lemon tree in the neighbouring garden of the Villa Florita. I closed my eyes. The sun came out again, moving quickly, and was on my face, burning. I changed my position on the seat. The sun was once again hidden behind cloud, the air was chill again, the flax rustled with a brittle snapping sound and the secretive small birds once again began their whispering and chittering. I fell asleep. And when I woke I shivered with cold. The mountains were harsh and grey with fallen used daylight, softened in the crevices with the blue of distance and evening.

So that was the Rose Hurndell Room! I dreamed of it, and of my own home in Bannockburn Road, Blenheim, and the two lives I had known there, and the daily use which marriage makes, one of the other, as the light makes of the twin slopes of the mountain, and I was glad that the colour of distance was beginning to touch my view of my life in Bannockburn Road. I dreamed of Brian's house in Baltimore, and of the front window massed with plants. And of my home in Stratford, once again near the railway line and the bracken, with the hay-fever trees, white-blossoming, growing everywhere, and the light green pine mysteriously transplanted from some Spanish island, growing in the front garden. Finally, in that disturbed night when I was partly awake and partly asleep, I thought of the blankets.

Unlike the deal tables of fiction and the drain-layer and French master, the debt collector, the inhabitants of Blenheim, of Baltimore, of Berkeley, and I as other than Violet Pansy Proudlock, ventriloquist or gossiping Alice Thumb, a secret-sharer of limited imagining, the blankets were real, with real history and real power of warming. I thought of those in my home in New Zealand, gathered from many places, from our old home in the south, from my parents' bed – coarse blankets matted with being washed and almost threadbare in places, faded from white to yellow with age and sun and hanging year after year on the clothes-line, strung between two appletrees, tautened and lifted into the arms of the wind by the manuka clothes-prop, returning to sag and swing close to the earth with the weight of the wetness. Their brand names were marked in the corners. Some were English – *Wilton* – a name I had heard spoken with the reverence obviously due to it; others, with names that caused a shiver of homesickness, a memory of school days when places became their products – Onehunga, Mosgiel, Kaiapoi: the places with the woollen mills and therefore the blankets. I remember my mother looking out at the fluffy-clouded sky with its patches of pale blue, saying, 'It's blanket weather.' That meant washing. The washing was a remembered ritual and risk. The women's magazines printed regularly long serious articles with such titles as, 'Dare I Wash My Woollen Blankets?' and 'The Risk of Washing Woollen Blankets,' sometimes pages of 'Hints On Washing Woollen Blankets.'

Blankets in their washing and drying were part of the poetry of the outside world and its weather.

> 'the white sheet bleaching on the hedge
> with Heigh the sweet birds how they sing'

It seemed that, among all the products of the earth, wool was the most important, especially when our early education dealt largely with products, with the implication that living depended less upon the heartbeat and import and export of breath than upon the import and export of products: wool, butter, mutton. In recent years there was even a prime minister who came from the home of blankets – *Kaiapoi*, and brought, naturally, a new share of warmth and compassion to the nation. How could he help it, coming from *Kaiapoi*?

But the price of wool! The cost of the warmth has always been too great. I know, who live outside fiction where the cold wind blows across the waste spaces from heart to heart.

Finally, I dreamed of the Garretts' golden blanket which everyone had wanted, I knew. I knew just as surely that it was mine, that it would take its place among the other treasured blankets in my home – that grey pair which I bought one week in a silverfish and ant-infested seaside beach in the north, the relic of a cold wet summer, when Lewis was alive, and the children were small, and we all lay shivering in our dripping hammocky beds, and the manuka and the sea outside were full of misty rain. And there was the purple blanket that was returned to me when the writer I met on my first visit to New York died suddenly. I gave it to her after I had stayed in her apartment, but after she moved from there, something happened, she couldn't find enough warmth, though the world was crying out for warmth and wool, and so, they told me, she stayed all day in her new apartment with the curtains drawn, the radio playing the black power station (in the days when black Americans, flying to San Francisco, could still be paged, unthinkingly, to 'come to the white courtesy telephone'), and with bottles of tranquillizers and fuming low-calorie sodas ranged along the window-sills. Beatrice, married at sixteen, divorced, a daughter at college. Beatrice, writing her novel, playing her music, perpetually depressed. They found her body in the East River. The purple blanket might have warmed her, but in the end there was no room left in her hibernating, winter heart for further cold seasons. Yes, her purple blanket is now safe at my home in Taranaki, with the other relics of warmth. And soon the gold blanket would be there too, I thought. I'm sure I smiled in my sleep realizing that I had won the gold blanket from the guests; unfairly, perhaps, but the price of warmth is often too high for too close a scrutiny of the means of getting it.

28.

In London I planned to find work and to discover by objective means whether I had ever suffered from schizophrenia. I hoped to take advantage of the offer from John Forrest to arrange an appointment for me at the Institute of Psychiatry. Although I was still inclined to cherish the distorted 'privilege' of having schizophrenia because it allied me with the great artists more readily than my attempts to produce works of art might have done, I suspected that my published writing might destroy that tenuous alliance, for I could not people, everlastingly, my novels with characters suffering from the 'Ophelia syndrome' with details drawn from my observations in hospital. I knew that the Ophelia syndrome is a poetic fiction that nevertheless usefully allows a writer to explore varieties of otherwise unspoken or unacceptable feelings, thoughts, and language.

I planned also to find an agent who would submit *Owls Do Cry* to English and American publishers while, supported by my earnings from a job, I continued writing my poems, stories, and the novel I had begun before I left New Zealand – *Uncle Pylades*.

My next preoccupation, as a result of my love affair in Ibiza, my parting from Bernard, my shortlived pregnancy, and my too ready acceptance of El Vici Mario as my future husband, was my need to gain more than an elementary knowledge of female and male anatomy and sexual practices: my ignorance even in my pretended state of 'sophisticated woman' had been appalling.

And so with Patrick Reilly's faithful and sometimes misdirected help, I began to study the Situations Vacant columns of the *South London Press* while Patrick, as before, like a conformist New Zealand conscience that had somehow travelled with me and assumed human shape, kept reminding me, 'You want a good steady job. A typist or secretary. You don't want to spend your time writing. There's no money in it. And it's not savoury.'

Obediently I went with him to the Labour Exchange in Vauxhall Road ('for the better type of worker, temp or permanent') where my nervousness made me unable to pass the typing test without making too many mistakes.

'What about Peek Frean's then?'

Ah, Peek Frean's! Perhaps to Patrick the London equivalent of Figuretti's. I thought nostalgically of my early days in London, of Patrick's dominating kindness and his continued reference to Peek Frean's – the biscuit (digestive, dark chocolate), the biscuit factory, even the factory premises, and how I'd been haunted by the name – Peek Frean's, with the other London names Tooting Bdy, Hatfield North, Crystal Palace, High Barnet . . . these names returned with renewed power.

I murmured, knowing Patrick would reply, 'Peek Frean's.'

'Yes, Peek Frean's. You could work in the biscuit factory.'

I did not take Patrick's advice; instead, I answered an advertisement for a writer of a fashion catalogue with a mail order firm in Brixton, and after an interview with Mr Jones when I flipped through a copy of *Owls Do Cry* saying casually that I had written the book, and noting that he appeared to be impressed, I was given the job, with a copy of an old catalogue for me to study and learn the descriptions of clothing. I would work with others in a large room; writing from 'nine till five'.

It was the presence of 'others' that deterred me. I explained that I had found other work.

Next, as I was now living near the South London Hospital for Women which advertised constantly for domestic help, I applied for work as a part-time wardsmaid but my interview with the matron resulted in her advising me to apply for nursing training as she considered me to be 'good nursing material'. The older students in their late twenties and early thirties, she said, were more able to apply themselves to study and practical work: she was sure I would make an excellent nurse. I would need a medical certificate of course, but that would be no problem as I appeared to be a healthy, intelligent, capable young woman.

The ideas and the flattery lured me. I made an appointment for a medical examination, choosing a doctor with rooms nearby, and with a name that sounded absurdly fictional, and that I now reduce, for obvious reasons, to initials. Dr C S. My medical examination was never conducted because I made the mistake of disclosing my 'mental history', whereupon Dr C S, instantly alarmed and horrified, her horror mixed with sympathy, exclaimed that nursing was not for me. She scanned my face for 'signs' of my prolonged incarceration and what had caused it; I knew better than to say it had been a 'mistake'.

Quickly she began ushering me to the door where she paused, perhaps slightly ashamed of her haste and her ill-concealed fear. She did have a friend, she said, who wanted a maid for light domestic help, and perhaps I could work there . . . under supervision, of course. Otherwise . . . with my history . . . my condition . . .

She ushered me quickly out the door.

I remember that interview vividly: its essence is contained in the peculiarly fictional name of Dr C S. Among my memories of London names it has a place beside Peek Frean's, Tooting Bdy, Tufnell Park . . . except that unlike these it encloses a small globule of horror.

It was not only the evil of conformity in the shape of Patrick Reilly that pursued me; my own past, too, continued to loom. How could I regain my confidence when I had never been able to tell 'my side' of the story? I knew it was time for me to find out 'the truth'.

Therefore I arranged through John Forrest an appointment with Dr Michael Berger of the Institute of Psychiatry.

In the meantime I found a job, a literary agent, and I bought an encyclopaedia of sex.

* * *

I became an usherette at the Regal Theatre, Streatham (women were known by the diminutive form of the word – *usherette*), where I began each day at half-past ten to prepare for the eleven o'clock session, with a break in the afternoon, and on alternate days I'd work the five o'clock or the seven o'clock session, sometimes both, finishing after eleven o'clock at night, after the routine search of the theatre for stray patrons, lost property; and newborn babies in the lavatory. I tried to enjoy the work for it was no doubt a 'broadening of experience' but it was not pleasant being in charge of a theatreful of children during the Saturday morning sessions or trying to control the teddy boys and girls in the Sunday afternoon sex-and-horror movies, or, during the intervals, playing the role of ice-maiden with my tray of orange drink, choc ices and plain ices strapped around my waist and over my shoulders and my hands in the half-dark trying to choose the correct change from my 'float', and then, later, having to pay money because I had confused the massive two shilling pieces with New Zealand halfcrowns. The staff and the audience fascinated me. In my role of 'developing writer' I 'studied' them carefully while I learned the language and ways of usherettes, how ushering in the counties was simply another job but ushering in the London suburbs was a prelude to ushering in the theatres like the Leicester Square where premieres were staged and film stars, directors, producers, made personal appearances and where an usherette at the right place and time and creating an interesting impression might find herself noticed, spoken to, perhaps on her way to Hollywood, stardom . . . the big time. This was the dream of all the young usherettes who worked with me and no doubt it was a sustaining dream for those living in the bedsitters of Streatham, Brixton, Clapham, and there was always an imagined or real example of the usherette – 'you remember her . . . only two years ago . . . who'd have thought?' – who 'made good'.

I found the work tiring and depressing: cinemas were being closed, replaced by bingo halls, and with each change of programme the managers of the Regals, ABC's, Odeons and Gaumonts, threatened with the loss of their jobs, tried to devise a more spectacular promotion. One week fake lions roared in the foyer, children took part in impossible competitions that they could never win, reminding me of the games arranged by the picture theatres in my childhood in the days of the Depression when a letter missing from a sentence to be completed with a set of letters, meant, for us, almost life or death. During the three weeks that *The Curse of Frankenstein* played, vampires, stakes, silver bullets, a model of Frankenstein, all in a mixture of horror folklore, were displayed in the foyer. And all the while the manager, a short middle aged man with an upward gaze and sandy hair looked increasingly anxious; and the usherettes dreamed of the time in Hollywood.

One free day after having chosen from the *Artists' and Writers' Yearbook* an agent, A M Heath, who had been the agent of e e cummings, and therefore I reasoned, must be willing to deal with experimental writing, that is, sacrifice money for faith in a writer, I went to Dover Street to keep an appointment with Patience Ross, of A M Heath. I found the office near the top floor. The general air of disorderliness surprised me – manuscripts everywhere, some piled on the floor, some on shelves, newly published books with the gloss still on their jackets displayed on stands and upon the walls, in cases, on bookshelves; photos of authors, many authors, men and women, all unknown to me.

Patience Ross, wearing black and grey with grey short hair, grey eyes, and a kindly manner, greeted me.

My first literary agent!

She reached into a large handbag crammed with books and drew out the copy of *Owls Do Cry* that she had been reading. She had been impressed by it, she said, although she did not suppose it would be of popular interest. If I agreed to allow them to be my agents they would begin submitting the book to English publishers and, through their agent in the United States, to American publishers, although I must bear in mind that publishers preferred to handle manuscripts and not books already published in another country. Did I realize, she asked, that under my contract with Pegasus Press they would be entitled to fifty percent of all my earnings from overseas? The prospect of royalties being so distant I merely smiled with an air of 'who cares?'

After the interview we left the office together in the openwork cast iron lift which Patience Ross compared to 'something out of Kafka' whereupon I, eager to appear 'like a writer' to match those daunting literary portraits on the office walls, murmured knowingly, 'Yes, Kafka . . .'

I caught the 137 bus back to Clapham South.

My next task was accomplished swiftly. I walked into a shop in Charing Cross Road and bought a large volume, the *Encyclopaedia of Sex*, advertised in the window as having 'hundreds of diagrams and photos in colour'.

I then prepared to keep my appointment for the following week with Dr Berger.

It was my first London summer with the heat oppressively full of fumes and the pavements burning. On the day of my appointment with Dr Berger at the Maudsley Hospital, Denmark Hill, I walked from Clapham South to Clapham North along Clapham Park Road and Acre Lane, through Brixton along Coldharbour Lane to Camberwell Green, past the rows of dilapidated brick houses; everywhere was grim, dirty with an air of poverty; the voices were strange, the woman in the shops said 'luv', 'Here you are, luv,' when I bought a packet of peppermints, *Curiously Strong*; the women wore headscarves, their faces looked tired; the men were pale, of small build, like burrow animals; beggars sat on the pavement, with cap or tin beside them, waiting for money to be thrown in response to the placard propped against the wall beside them – *War Wounded, Stumps For Legs. Blind From Birth. Born This Way. A Wife and Five Children.*

I passed a shop that advertised *Horse Flesh For Human Consumption*. I read the notices in the newsagents, and the chalked menus outside the uninviting transport cafés. I arrived at a square of dried grass bordered with a few shrubs and seats and surrounded by traffic going to Peckham, Forest Hill, Central London, Clapham. I walked up the street to the outpatient department of the Maudsley Hospital where I hoped to find at last the answers to the questions I still asked myself about my 'history'. I had to know whether my own views, usually met with polite disbelief or sometimes with sceptical agreement, held any truth or were merely another instance of self-deception.

During my first interview with Dr Berger I found myself again in the familiar role of using my long stay in hospital as a means of holding his attention. I knew that such a long stay with such drastic treatments performed and planned, usually gave the conclusion that my condition had been hopeless, as well as the surmise that it could recur: I knew the effect on strangers of learning about my past. I also knew that their response could be used to accomplish my wishes. The fact that, invariably, I was forced to go to such lengths to uncover my 'secret, true' self, to find the answers to questions that, had I the confidence and serenity of being myself 'in the world' could have been asked directly, was evidence to me of a certain unhealthy self-burial. Often, after repeated earthquakes, there is little sign of what survives beneath the ruins, and if there are survivors they must first attract attention before the authorities decide to investigate and explore the remains of the city, whether it be a real or a mirror city that moves when the wind moves and is subjected to tides of ocean and sky.

Dr Berger, a tall dark pale man, with a chillingly superior glance and quellingly English voice, made another appointment to see me. Feelings of past unpleasantness and fear had been roused in me by this visit to a psychiatrist: attracting his attention and observing his serious face had reduced my store of confidence. I knew, however, that if anyone could discover the 'truth' it would be he, alone or with his colleagues.

I continued to work at the Regal Theatre. My supply of money was fast running out, and ushering became more tedious and depressing as each afternoon during the coffee break I listened to the confidences of the younger usherettes. One had been going to bed with a famous singer whom everyone thought of as perfect, you could see his kindly face on the television each evening: he had promised her a contract and, perhaps, stardom, she said. Another, learning that I hoped to be a writer, brought her collection of poems for me to read and I winced as I followed her golden moon to the month of June and looked into her lover's eyes that were blue as skies; yet perhaps I need not have winced had I thought of my own experiences.

Sometimes my father in Oamaru sent a bundle of five shilling postal notes bought on separate days and 'saved' during the currency restrictions. Miss Lincoln at Mt Maunganui also sent her bundle of five shilling postal notes.

And in the evening when Patrick Reilly and I were not working, we walked on the Common as in the days when I first came to London, and it was nearing that time of year, the blemished summer finally promising to give way in a cloud of dust and withering leaves, with the suddenly blood-filled sun stalking the city in and out through the thinning branches of the plane trees; and soon the grass on the Common would lie sparse, brown, with no hope of further growth.

I kept my second appointment with Dr Berger. I, who had been absorbing the city of London in its seasons, spoke as if I were the city, revealing myself as tired, looking towards winter. I talked of suicide. Such talk came readily to me as a shortcut to ensure action when the paths to real communication had been overgrown. I knew that talk of suicide must always be taken seriously, that it is only the uninformed who do otherwise or respond, to their later regret, with calm acceptance of the fact and the possibility of the deed. Such acceptance, an assurance that all is well, is enough to precipitate the act in a desperate person who then has no other way of making known the desperation.

It was Dr Berger's opinion that I should become a patient at the Maudsley for observation and tests. My plan had succeeded. I would now have my questions answered. Although I had many fears, I supposed that this famous Institute of Psychiatry would have few of the shortcomings of New Zealand hospitals, that it would have many doctors trained to make thorough diagnoses after learning all the facts of each case; also that, unlike in New Zealand, the 'case' would have a chance to speak, to be known at first hand. I expected much.

Dr Berger allowed me to return to my room in Clapham South where I collected a few personal belongings, and explained to Patrick who offered to store my suitcases in his room for the six weeks I'd be in hospital. In spite of my growing apprehension I did feel my action was necessary: I would at last find out 'the truth'.

* * *

I had not known what to expect from the Maudsley. What I found impressed me and gave me cause for gratitude that I still feel. There was then an abundance of medical, nursing, domestic staff with many of the nurses from Europe, Africa, Ireland, the West Indies, and one or two from New Zealand. In the admission and observation ward the ratio was one nurse to five patients with domestic duties given to ward-maids, kitchen maids, cooks, leaving the nurses free for professional nursing. Remembering my days in the Seacliff Hospital in New Zealand, in the 'back ward' where the nurses were forbidden to talk to me (I was told this later by two nurses, now retired), I was amazed to discover that here at the Maudsley it was the nurses' duty to talk to the patients, to get to know them – how else could a correct diagnosis be made? I was impressed also to find that the patients were interviewed by their doctor several times a week, at first daily, and not, as happened in New Zealand, once on admission, once on discharge, with occasional fatuous 'Hellos' between, no matter how many years the interval 'between' may have been. At the Maudsley I would have no reason to complain that decisions were made about me without anyone having taken the time and trouble to speak to me and try to know me. The Maudsley also gave numerous standard 'tests' as an aid to diagnosis (another method unheard of or at least not practised during my years in New Zealand hospitals).

There was an element of luxury, even of self-indulgence, in having a personal doctor and nurse. I was assigned a Dr Alan Miller, a young American graduate to whom I gave my personal history (omitting the large mass of the untellable) during frequent interviews. The Maudsley had already obtained from New Zealand details of my period in hospitals there, of diagnosis, treatment, prognosis.

Dr Miller was a tall burly man who was feeling the cold of the approaching English winter, and so appeared to be wearing many layers of clothes, increasing his bulk. He worried about his weight. He often ate chocolate bars during our interviews. For recreation he played the viola and was proud to correspond once a year with Pablo Casals. He had brought his wife, his children and his American Ford station wagon for his year at the Maudsley, and was lamenting that his year would be over soon. Although finding out such details about a psychiatrist was not usual, Dr Miller talked freely about himself and his feelings and opinions in contrast to the serious sober Englishmen who stared, frowned, half-smiled, and uttered only 'M-m, I see.' I was grateful to have as my doctor someone who was not afraid to acknowledge and voice the awful thought that he belonged, after all, to the human race, that there was nothing he could do about it, and pretending to be a god could never change it. And how enthusiastic Dr Miller was! 'You've never suffered from schizophrenia,' he said. 'Schizophrenia is a terrible illness.' The verdict had to be objective, however, the result of tests and observations and interviews with the team of doctors supervised by Dr Berger, with the results to be given at a meeting chaired by Sir Aubrey Lewis, then director of the hospital. Infected by Dr Miller's enthusiasm I performed and underwent tests of many kinds, mental, manual. I had my first electroencephalogram (a test which should have been given as routine years ago) and I was disconcerted when Dr Miller, always eager to communicate the results, announced that my brainwaves were 'more normal than normal', thus shattering my long-held acquaintance and kinship with Van Gogh, Hugo Wolf – inspired to blossom by the unforgettable words of the handsome charming young lecturer of years ago – 'When I think of you I think of Van Gogh, Hugo Wolf . . . Janet you are suffering from a loneliness of the inner soul . . .'

Finally I was summoned to the interview room where the medical team sat at a long table with Sir Aubrey Lewis at the head. The team had already had its meeting and formed its conclusions, and after a few minutes' conversation with me, Sir Aubrey gave the verdict. I had never suffered from schizophrenia, he said. I should never have been admitted to a mental hospital. Any problems I now experienced were mostly a direct result of my stay in hospital.

I smiled. 'Thank you,' I said shyly, formally, as if I had won a prize.

Later, Dr Miller triumphantly repeated the verdict. I recall his expression of delight, and the way he turned bulkily in his chair because his layers of clothes appeared to hinder his movement.

'England's cold,' he said. 'I have this thick woollen underwear.' The latest fashions, short overcoats, narrowed trouser legs, added to his discomfort. Perhaps I remember so vividly Dr Miller's layers of clothes worn against the winter season because I myself had suddenly been stripped of a garment I had worn for twelve or thirteen years – my schizophrenia. I remembered how wonderingly, fearfully I had tried to pronounce the word when I first learned of the diagnosis, how I had searched for it in psychology books and medical dictionaries, and how, at first disbelievingly, then surrendering to the opinion of the 'experts', I had accepted it, how in the midst of the agony and terror of the acceptance I found the unexpected warmth, comfort, protection: how I had longed to be rid of the opinion but was unwilling to part with it, and even when I did not wear it openly I always had it by for emergency, to put on quickly, for shelter from the cruel world. And now it was gone, not destroyed by me and my constant pleading for 'the truth' allied to an unwillingness to lose so useful a protection, but banished officially by experts: I could never again turn to it for help.

The loss was great. At first, the truth seemed to be more terrifying than the lie. Schizophrenia, as a psychosis, had been an accomplishment, removing ordinary responsibility from the sufferer. I was bereaved. I was ashamed. How could I ask for help directly when there was 'nothing wrong with me'? How could I explain myself when I could no longer move cunningly but necessarily from the status of a writer to one of having schizophrenia, back and forth when the occasion *suited*? The official plunder of my self-esteem was eased by the attitude of the staff at the hospital. As Professor Lewis had said, I did need professional help to free myself from the consequences of my long stay in hospital; in the meantime I would remain in the Maudsley while my interviews with Dr Miller continued. Once he had learned of the background of my life we talked mostly of everyday matters of the present, in a formless kind of therapy that allowed inclusion of worries of the present and of the past. We calmly dragged the lake, as it were, and watched the fireflies and the sunlight on the water, and usually let the old dead rest and the discovered dead return to their depths, while the water, momentarily clouded, cleared and became still. The one prolonged difficulty in our talks was my panic, scarcely comprehended or admitted, at the loss of my schizophrenia and my unwillingness to let it go, my urging, out of habit and a need for warmth, that maybe it was there after all, forever a part of my life?

I spent the winter cocooned in the warmth of the Maudsley. I became friends with the nurses and patients and with the kitchenmaid from Germany, *Gerda*, who enveloped everyone with kindness – 'Oh, Janet, mein goodness kinder,' she'd say, smiling.

I have heard that the time when the hospital was fully staffed did pass; then, in the late nineteen fifties the staff were all highly qualified and diverse with the foreign nurses and psychiatrists bringing an extra dimension of their culture to their work. A particular example of the strength and wisdom of the management of the Maudsley was the inclusion of doctors who were themselves handicapped by disabilities, and it was often these doctors who became more easily able to communicate with their patients.

I was now preparing to leave hospital to continue with my 'own life'. It was early spring, with occasional snowstorms. Rather too directly for my comfort, Dr Berger explained that as a prelude to my 'holding down a job' he had asked Miss Baer, the librarian, to give me work in the medical library. Although it was known that I'd had two books published in New Zealand and I had an ambition to write full time, there was little evidence in the harsh publishing world of London that I would be able to make a career of writing. I had heard from Patience Ross of A M Heath that up to fifty publishers in the United States and in the United Kingdom had admired my *Owls Do Cry* but declined to publish it, and therefore, in some dejection, but maintaining my 'poetic' stance, I went to work in the medical library only to find, a few days later, that I was pronounced 'unsuitable'. Dr Berger then gave me the task of cataloguing medical papers in the brain museum. The brain museum! Blissfully alone, I spent many days sorting through medical journals in the company of glass display cases filled with preserved, labelled tumours and brains. I learned from studying the journals that ECT (Electric Shock or Convulsive Therapy) was commended as a means of provoking *fear* in the patient, the fear being as it were a *bonus*, and salutary – for the psychiatrist no doubt and not for the patient! Sitting there among the labelled, bottled brains I ventured to hope for the quality of strength and vigilance in psychiatrists, their continued examination and testing of their humanity without which they might become political operators infected with the endemic virus of psychiatry, politics, and some other professions – belief in the self as God.

29.

I brought a leper into my house.
I gave him the spare room, with the panel-end bed, the flock mattress, the spare blankets and sheets
and the duchesse with the oval mirror
that, swinging back and forth, reflects a person from head to foot.

'I have travelled a long way,' my leper said.
'I had to wait many years before they gave me a permit to come here.

I had to be investigated, examined,
sponsored,
and then at last
I was accepted.
I shall get treatment here
from the hospital on Cumberland Street.
I shall sleep in your spare room, have meals with you,
walk down through the Botanical Gardens under the
  Ponderosa Pine trees
across the bridge
past the Otago Savings Bank Centennial Kiosk
past the pensioners' houses on Duke Street.
And then one day when I am cured I will go to the Labour
  Exchange and find a job.
How happy I am to be accepted into your country!'

The neighbour clipping his hedge looked over at me.
'I hear you've a leper staying with you,' he said. 'Isn't it
  dangerous?'
I answered with the best argument.
'Oh they wouldn't have admitted my leper if they thought
  that.' I said.
'You know they're very careful about that sort of thing.'
'I suppose you must be right,' my neighbour said. 'All the
  same I'd watch out if I were you.'

The woman tending the deep-freeze in the grocer's lifted the
steak and egg sausage carefully out its
bed beside the chicken and onion sausage.
'I hear you've a visitor,' she said. 'Is he staying long?'
'Oh he's making his home here.'
'He's from overseas?'
'Yes. My leper. He's come to be cured.'
The woman frowned. 'Yes, I've heard that,' she said.
And after I began to walk from the shop I noticed she rubbed
her hands on a small towel hanging on a rail behind the door.

The front of my house reeked of disinfectant.

Men from the Council
had arrived and were cleaning the footpath.
'The city's taking no chances,' the foreman said.

Months passed. Spring came, and summer, and autumn, and winter when the rain stayed clogged in the long grass and the dead leaves flapped against the twigs
and fog, mingled with smoke, settled like snow in the valleys.
My leper was stricken with a strange disease
that none could diagnose.
It was, they said, a disease
worse than leprosy, worse than any other,
hardest to be cured of,
a fatal disease where the sufferer may yet last a lifetime
in agony and mutilation.

They said he had caught the disease from the neighbours cutting the hedges,
from the woman serving in the deep-freeze counter in the grocer's, from the Council men spraying disinfectant outside my front door, and – worst blow of all – they said he had caught it from me, from my use of the possessive pronoun.
'Did you not talk of him,' they reminded me, 'as *your* leper?
My leper, you said. *My* leper this and that.
The disease of being at once outlawed and owned is worse than leprosy.
It is, simply, terribly,
the indestructible virus.'
The gift of the living who are blind
to the living who are believed dead.

30.

Then almost two weeks before her departure she accepted an invitation from the Hanuere family to spend the afternoon and the night, if she wished, at their home up the river a hundred kilometres north of Puamahara. They had sold the dairy, they said, and were shifting north, although Hene and sometimes Hare stayed to train the new owners. Up the river, Mattina and a party of the Hanueres' friends from Wellington would have a meal, enjoy a few games to raise funds for the old people to buy their pensioner flats instead of renting them from the government; and in the evening they would catch up on news, sing, entertain, be entertained, and sleep.

'Do come,' Hene had urged. 'See how we live when we're not in Kowhai Street. See the way of life of our people.'

Mattina hesitated.

'But I don't know the language.'

Hene laughed. 'Neither do I. I'm learning. And the best way to learn is on the marae. And don't worry, it's quite informal.'

Perhaps, Mattina thought, she might learn more of the legend of the Memory Flower, for the Maoris were the people of the land who held or harboured a source of memory which the latecomers, the other immigrants, were only now learning to seek and share. Mattina knew that New Zealanders of all races had reached a self-consciousness of an identity they had been struggling for years to find and capture, and now they had captured it, they dressed it in fashionable ideas and feelings and drew attention to it and congratulated themselves on their discovery, on its presence; and fortunately, the sensitivity of growth and maturity was tempering and softening and lighting with imagination what may have caused (and did cause) shame, guilt, denial, the refusal of ignorance to *know*. There were people of many races in Puamahara. One noticed them as one did not notice, say, in the United Nations city of New York. People in Puamahara turned to stare at unfamiliar dress and accents. It seemed to Mattina that every wave of fashion in everything – people, new forms of art, poetry, language behaviour, dress – had set out ten or twenty years earlier, and now washed about the shores of New Zealand; also, there was still the flowing colonial wave from 'elsewhere' – even casting up visitors like Mattina herself who came to 'study' the distant foreigners. There was now, however, another wave often more hoped for and talked about than real, but visible in the land itself, flowing from the land and having been there for centuries concealed often by the more visible waves from elsewhere. It was now flowing in its own power, inwards and outwards, reaching the shores of the Northern Hemisphere.

A station wagon already packed with guests arrived outside Number Twenty-four. Mattina, with a paper bag of food that she felt might be welcome, and her handbag (known as her 'pocketbook'), but not the requested sleeping-bag, stood by the mailbox and stared self-consciously at the crowded van.

'You sit up front with Piki and me,' Hene said. 'Hare's at the back with the others. Hey you kids. Take care of those kittens.'

Hene then introduced her relatives from Wellington.

'The kittens are Ngeru and Boy George,' Hene said.

Looking back into the van Mattina saw two thin black kittens each wrapped in a piece of blanket and being cuddled by each of the two little girls.

'Are we all set? You lot OK in the back?'

They travelled the long straight West Coast Road through bleak plains where the wind, roaming unchecked by the usual mass of huge dark-green trees, buffeted every car and cycle, and the van rocked from side to side as if it were a flimsy boat on a vast sea. They passed through a faded city of stone houses with hundred-year-old trees arched above the streets with their branches entwined, and in the parks many-trunked old trees with their heads far in the sky and their branches covered with dark-red blossoms. Then, beyond the city, along the winding path of the river, they travelled an uneven makeshift road, and soon stands of bush replaced the stone city and the polluted flotsam-filled river became clear blue and green and curved closely against the earth like a greenstone necklace; the hills now rose tall, big-boned, angled, showing hints of green, burned in places, elsewhere matted with golden grass or tussock with darker bush shadowed in the steep valleys. On the tip of one slope a head-shaped boulder was sculptured from the rock; one could imagine the face staring north-east to the volcanic peaks and mountains of the interior of the North Island that, like all interiors, was steeped in legend, as if once the glance of the sea is left behind, the glance of the unknown secret places of the earth and sky intensifies and is directed upon those who live in the interior and upon the traveller, the stranger, who leaves with a heart imprinted with the glance, and an urge to return again and again, and to tell of the journey, beginning, 'When I was in the interior . . . of the North Island of New Zealand . . . of the Andes . . . of the Rocky Mountains . . . of the Carpathians. . . .' The coast-dwellers absorb their own secret though the eyelid of the watching sea never closes upon them, but when its eye can no longer follow them, its immediate fury is diffused across the seas of the world; different, indeed, from the eye of the interior which smoulders even in the traveller's absence, day and night, century after century.

The day was sunny, the sky pale blue. They arrived at a small village set beside the river between two steep hills rising from a small plain that was partly cultivated with fruit trees and vegetable and flower gardens, while the land nearer the river held about six dwellings, old, with corrugated iron roofs and weatherboards from which the paint had long ago faded and peeled. The houses were bare bones, unclad, untiled, with old-fashioned sash windows, the cords hanging broken.

'Only three families live here now,' Hene explained. 'But more are returning. We don't realize how unique it is until we leave it for the city. The Pakeha has nothing like this way of living – not here in New Zealand. I believe it's like a small English village without the post office, the pub and the general store.'

She pointed to a new stone structure backing on to one of weathered stone, with moss around the lower walls.

'There's the new kindergarten. And the old building's the church. The kindergarten belongs to the government,' she said with some bitterness. 'And those small pensioner flats – they're the government's too. I told you we're raising money to buy them. As for that kindergarten – the design is not of our choosing. We have our language nests now. Kohanga reo. Also we didn't want the Plunket Rooms here, with nurses coming to tell us what to do with our babies.'

Then she pointed to a group of young people working in the gardens.

'We've rescued them from the Court, from prison. Soon Hare and I will be working full time helping the young people. We rescue Pakeha kids too, and we bring them up here but after a few weeks the novelty seems to wear off and they get homesick, not always for their home but to be on their own, not always in a group the way it is here, the way it is with us. Some of my people don't like to be in a group but usually it's the Pakeha way. I've seen them come here invited to stay, and they're on cloud nine; then they get restless, they want to be somewhere else, they've had Maoritanga for the time being, thank you, and yet if you happen to be among a group of people at a function you hear the same people holding forth about having "been on the marae" and how wonderful it is, and how much they learned – which they did – and others look enviously at them – well, we're all a bit that way, I suppose; some people are hard to understand; even the elders of my own people don't seem to understand what *I'm* doing.'

She looked shrewdly at Mattina.

'Forgive me for being frank,' she said. 'Funnily enough, it's visitors like you who get to know more about us than many of those who live here. The novelty, I suppose. The tribes of the far south on that TV programme *The Beautiful World*, eh? We're distant enough from the rest of the world to be thought not to have feelings and lives of our own: both us and the Pakehas are at the long end of the poking stick – Look, they move, they speak, they walk, they think. Isn't it so, that the further away you are, the less you are known, the more easily you may lose your state of being human? For some of us, we've already lost it in our own land. I know it's hard to think of separate individuals in a country thousands of miles away just as it's hard to think of separate numbers among millions – the millions wipe out the handful – where's three dollars among three billion? There was a time, you see, when this country and both Maori and Pakeha and others were nothing because we thought we were so far away – far away from the rulers, the seat of Empire; but now we're ourselves, and we can't be ignored or made nothing and no one, because the distance has gone.'

Hene looked thoughtful.

'When we do become far away from ourselves we become nothing. And if we are far from God, it's not God who does the abolishing, it's us.'

'Oh,' Mattina said, not wanting to get into a discussion on religion. She was rescued by the announcement through a megaphone that the two competitions had begun – guess the weight of a sheep, and drive ten nails the fastest into a block of wood.

'This is to keep us busy while the hangi is being prepared,' Hene said. 'And raise money too.'

'Let's guess the weight of a sheep,' someone said.

Hene, her cousin Riki, and her cousin Rua, in her seventies, known as Aunty Rua, came to the small pen where an 'older' ewe with a ragged dirty coat stood chewing her cud as she watched the watchers guessing her weight. Now and then she stamped her foot, voicing her authority and impatience. Her mysterious glinting eyes like polished stone looked everywhere and nowhere; her long nose sniffed disapproval. Unlike many other captives, the ewe did not butt at her enclosure or trot round and round in panic; gathering more than its own fortitude, indeed, drawing from the fund of all animals that are bred to be killed and eaten, the ewe neatly tucked in her forelegs and sank to the ground on the scattering of straw, without relaxing the glittering suspicion in her eyes.

'It'll be harder to guess her weight now she's sitting down,' Riki said.

Each wrote their chosen number of kilograms on a sheet of paper, which they folded and dropped in a cardboard box.

'The next time we do this,' Hene said laughing, 'is at the General Election. Guess the weight of the sheep.'

There was some bitterness in her voice.

'The country's in a turmoil,' she said to Mattina. 'We're in the kind of state where we now believe everything they tell us and absorb like blotting paper all their fine promises.'

As soon as they had made their guess, the contest closed, the sheep was weighed, and no one had guessed correctly. They fell silent as if the weight they offered had been returned to their mood, threefold or sevenfold or some other magical number. Then each brightened as the imagined complication of winning became more burdensome than that of losing. Only Hene said practically that she would have added the ewe to their small flock next to the vegetable gardens. The ewe would have been named, introduced to Geraldine the nanny goat and Oscarine and Kaiwai the cows.

The food for the hangi was lifted and served. While most of the company sat inside at the long tables, several including Mattina and Rua sat outside in the sun, on the long wooden seats ranged against the wall. By the time Mattina had her paper plate filled, the pork was lukewarm but the kumara and potatoes were like hot pebbles. The dark green vegetable called *puha* was tasty, gritty and strong like aged spinach, and all the food was smooth and slippery with juices and melted fats. What bliss, Mattina thought, as she picked up the pieces of pork with her fingers and sucked in the juices and the tender strips; and listened to the rushing of the river near where the dark green wing of the hill cast its shade and shelter only so far as not to disturb the sun-filled marae. The shrieks of the children; the barking of the black dogs that looped here and there chasing thrown sticks; the sweet taste of the meal; the old houses, their timber grey as if they were the most ancient trees; the walls encircling the houses like large faded aprons; beneath the commotion of eating, talk, laughing, the animals, the river, Mattina felt the presence of a yesterday's silence that brought a hunger to the back of her throat: a world-hunger.

She looked at Rua sitting beside her and smiled.

'Not like America, eh?' Rua said.

Mattina again became the researcher, the foreigner.

'It's marvellous here. And Hene tells me you teach flax weaving?'

'Riki and I both teach,' Rua said. 'Riki is our cousin, as you know. He was kept in a mental hospital from age fifteen, and only last year someone noticed him there – thirty years later! – and said, "Hey why aren't you out in the world?" And of course Hene and Hare came to his rescue, and now he lives here, teaching weaving and making baskets, kete. He's a good boy.'

'Can you tell me something about flax weaving?'

Rua smiled. 'First,' she said, 'you must *know* flax. I know flax and flax knows me. You understand the sort of knowing I mean?'

'I do,' Mattina said, with rising excitement at the recognition that here was *her* kind of knowing; and that of the James family; and Hercus Millow; and of the others in Kowhai Street; the knowing that included but was not dependent on the Memory Flower or the Gravity Star; that by itself could banish distance, nearness, weight, lightness, up, down, today, yesterday, tomorrow.

Without binoculars, cameras.

Without the Memory Flower, the Gravity Star.

'The important thing to remember is that flax *knows* about you, your life, your secrets, and when you plant it, it's there watching you, knowing you; you can hide nothing from it. If it won't grow for you, you can be sure you have hurt it.'

'Oh,' Mattina said uneasily.

'Flax is always alive. See this kete?'

She held up a woven flax basket where she kept her sweater and pocketbook.

'This is alive, listening to us now. Yes, you must have a special feeling about flax to be able to grow it, cut it without making it bleed, scrape it without hurting it, and weave it without going against its wishes.'

Mattina was impressed. There was a warmth in Rua, a wisdom that could not be ignored. The others felt it too. From time to time the children came to climb on her lap and be hugged, or one of the men came to sit by her and talk earnestly about his or his family's problems, and leave laughing and making a gesture of triumph as if Rua's conversation or silence had given him new life and hope. She was like a public mother. No wonder she knew the secrets of flax and flax knew her. And seeing her surrounded by two or three generations, Mattina realised that in her time at Kowhai Street she had met only the two generations of families; no doubt if she stayed longer she would meet grandparents, uncles, aunts, cousins, brothers, sisters, and read them and know them as she was learning to know the parents and their children.

Later, after tea, scones and cakes, Mattina followed the others to a large room where, behind the scenes, members of the family had been arranging mattresses around the walls. She too chose a mattress and made herself comfortable, leaning on a pillow, with a rug over her, and when Rua chose the mattress beside her and began to point out and define the routine, Mattina felt an unaccountable gratitude, a feeling of having been honoured.

31.

A house without Yeats.

Oh, a wild swan or two and a paradisal Innisfree,
and age 'old and grey and full of sleep'
all Fleckered and Blundened, Monroed beautifully
safe in proportion within a seldom-used anthology
all written before the time of the towering fury
when even the gentle dolphins not singing but gonging
like emperors, tormented the sea.

A house without Yeats.
The prisoners surrender, go quietly.
No surprise at the sentence – what is a day, a year, what
  difference
but of indifference; and age a concealment, a verbal mask.

Hark the horns of Carmel are calling us to lifetime tenancy,
community sleep by a calm sea!
(They will sell this house and go soon to their chosen place in
Carmel,
the retirement home where there are suites and
pleasant rooms, single and shared.
A medical centre will they have there, a view of the sea from
the hill, and a promise of ripe old age, if they are spared.

And they shall have company there in the large community
room,
with colour TV and parlour games; and a corner just to sit
and ripen as in a kind of pretomb home
where they think and talk about death and begin to welcome it.

They will sell this house and go soon, for their
name's on the waiting list,
and they've paid a huge deposit for the suite with a view of
the shore, where a golden age awaits them in a cloud
of autumnal mist
arising from the gold decay of their deep hearts' ripened
core.)

A house without Yeats.
A house with everything – books, geraniums in bloom,
humming birds
at the throat of the morning flowers,
redwood trees, a patio, colour TV, a piano with leaves of music
(Largo, Oxen Minuet, Für Elise)
comfortable furniture, sculptured heads, paintings
and books on paintings.
Two large dictionaries.
House-trained house-plants; display alcoves, macramé
hangings; Mexican, Danish kitchenware; an Italian salad
basket,
Australian ginger,

English conserves.

A house without Yeats.
Turning the pages of the old school anthologies
I search for the wild swans, the bean rows, the sleeping old
men.

No rage. No towers.
Only the Garretts' lives demanding
I want a Shakespeare like the real Shakespeare
I want a miraculous marble table.
We have all, all, and 'the agony of flame that cannot singe a
sleeve.'

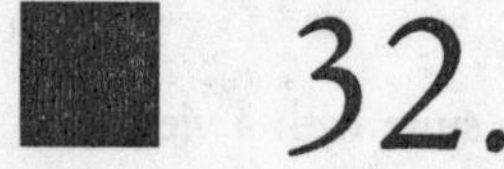

Each of us inherits for use in our death education a supply of private and public deaths as numerous and memorable as our supply of loves. If I search my own death store I find a collection representative of the kind most people have. In a country of earthquake and volcanic activity we naturally take imaginative possession of recent and remote upheavals from everywhere. I hold the Vesuvius eruptions as if I had lived through them. I see the sterilized pumice dead in all their poses of living and loving and I remember the childhood rumours that one could walk among the dead in Pompeii and break off pieces of people to take home as souvenirs (I did not realize that this is always the pastime of tourists), that a woman could scrub herself in her bath with a man's pumice testicles. At school, in history, I learned of the lava burial of my country's Pink and White Terraces which few in my generation had seen but which everyone spoke of with wonder and a sense of loss. In the same way I acquired earthquake deaths, the shipwrecked, the dead of many wars, of all wars, including the Crusades where the soldiers, knowing that death is 'heavier than the heaviness of all things,' dressed themselves in iron mail to die.

Then, with the invention of radio and television we were suddenly given more deaths than we could cope with, and now we not only inherited them, we are invited to witness them. Where the written word allows us to siphon off small doses of death, the image in the moving picture does not even wait to invite us, it abducts us to the scene with the result that we have a collection of unformed, ill-matured, ungrieved-over deaths in our storehouse and a scarcity of feelings to match them. The periods of grief, of mourning, are curtailed or lost, the death itself has no silence in which to become real; often our supply of feeling ceases, and aware of our poverty, while the deaths continue, we begin to hate; having no other feeling left to give to the demanding deaths we give ourselves, we become death as surely as those who love become the beloved, 'by just exchange one for another given.'

So I have shared these deaths by volcano, tidal wave, shipwreck, cyclone, all those acts described in steamship and air tickets as Acts of God, and many including genocide which are acts of man. The total confuses and sickens. We take out the dregs of feeling and gum them dutifully to the appropriate deaths, as if we were fixing stamps in a stamp collection, and we begin to fear that like the astronauts who walk on the moon we can do no more than record and file and exclaim, like creatures in a comic strip. It is not the birth explosion but the death explosion which threatens to bankrupt man of all that makes him human.

* * *

I remember that when I was a boy of ten – to me the strangest, most secretive, most impressionable age of boyhood – I watched in one afternoon a concentrated adhesiveness of living and dying. I was out in the street with my friends when two dogs began to copulate and instead of separating after a decent interval they stayed together, and at first we were not surprised, making bawdy remarks to one another about how they wanted to keep doing it because they liked it so much. But when they had been together about an hour and a half and were obviously struggling to separate, we stopped joking and became alarmed. A crowd had gathered. The adults among the crowd, not aware of our knowledge of these things, made stupid remarks about how hot it was and how the heat had melted the tar on the road and caused the dogs to stick together. In the background we made hee-heeing noises deploring this tiresome explanation. No one dared to say the truth – that the dogs in all their fossicking running up and down the streets and around corners and investigating the town, had found the best sticking place in each other. Why, then, we thought uneasily, could they not separate when they so obviously wanted to? They were back to back and struggling madly for release.

What a strange afternoon of adhesiveness! The time and manner of the dogs' eventual separation are buried by my pervading memory of the tedious waiting for their discomfort to be relieved, of the alarm in ourselves, the shocked reticence of the adults when they knew that we knew, and most of all by the example of another, deathly, adhesive at work at the same time, almost directly across the road, where a linesman had been repairing the electric wires. He had been busy, crouched at the top of the pole for some time, when a passerby, looking up, realized that the man was unconscious. An ambulance was summoned, and rescuers, and while the beasts on one side of the road struggled to sever their loving connection, the men opposite tried to release the embrace of death. I remember seeing the man crouched over the wires all the long hot afternoon, with the wires refusing to release his convulsed fingers and body. Again and again, or so I remember, the rescuers tried and failed to release him; he was held in a death lock. I remember my sick feeling, staring up at the crouched man, listening to the anguished doom-laden conversation of the watching small crowd who could do nothing to help. I longed for the linesman to be parted from the electric wires as I longed for the two struggling dogs to be separated.

There was a feeling as if the whole world had come alive and was preparing to reach out and grasp, as the plants do in the fairy tales, and not let go of us, its prey. The dogs had had their moments of loving, the man had had his moment of dying. Why did it not end, then and there? Why need loving and dying be such a state of prolonged attachment? I felt seized by an agonized imprisoned feeling. I wanted to free myself of the dogs, the man, the electricity greedy in the wires, the tar melting on the footpath, the soft bubbles of wet paint on the gatepost, the burnished summer flies that settled and would not be brushed off (we called them 'sticky flies'), the trailing plant that grew behind the hedge and clung to our flesh and clothes, forcibly emptying its nursery of seeds into our care whenever we touched it, the bluegum nuts which dug into us when we trod, leaving their starry shape imprinted on the soles of our feet. Escape seemed impossible.

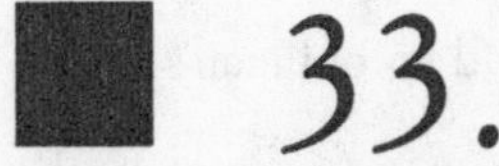

Dear First Dad, it is Christmas, family-time. Pain
and Santa, white and red are In,
getting down to it, distributing upon branches of green pine
the gifts guaranteed to break, stain, fit, keep warm,
beautify, startle, harm, amuse. The favour, your favour is
we never grew out of Christmas: hard bright gold blue
sea and sky Christmas; a swim and sunburn
snowcarols out of tune where the gold-brown cicadas
flake the sky, green crickets swarm
in the grass
carolling with their arse as men and women are doing
on the lupined beach. Our Christmas was
enjoy, swim, eat, sleep, wake to grief of destruction.
What was it? We had it. It is gone. Tears then,
tears, and a handkerchief for us and Uncle Leonard to fold
  the grief in

The annual lesson
of trying to throw a saltstorm of tears to catch time
or spreading a sticky mess like cake icing, pretend it is bird lime.

Growing up we grew in
like unhealthy finger and toenails;
you cut us to the quick
which was wrong, confusing the necessary
circle with the necessary straight line.

Hands touch. Hands and their fingers cling.
Feet stand to give the head
headroom an unacceptably lonely
distance from the sky. Clouds, head in.

Let the soldiers die, father, and the pears blossom and fruit
green and russet; decay is brown
like the earth and the singing cicadas and an old man's or
woman's
sparse pubic hair and skin
decay-spotted like the fallen pears.

Breathe in the gas mask, father,
or the poisonous air like a scorpion
stings your lung.

34.

That evening Mattina opened the typescript left by Dinny Wheatstone, and began to read:

'The human race is an elsewhere race and I am an imposter in a street of imposters. I am nothing and no one: I was never born. I am a graduate imposter, having applied myself from my earliest years to the study of the development of imposture as practised in myself and in others around me in street, town, city, country, and on earth. The imposture begins with the first germ of disbelief in being, in self, and this allied to the conviction of the "unalterable certainty of truth", produces the truth of disbelief, of deception of being, of self, of times, places, peoples, of all time and space. The existence of anything, of anywhere and anytime produces an instant denial only in graduates of imposture; in most others who remain unaware of such a state, particularly in themselves, there may be little or no knowledge of their reality, their nonentity.

'My qualification for writing this short narrative about the residents of Kowhai Street, Puamahara, is chiefly my imposture which as a result of my nonentity, is accompanied by an uncanny perception of human life, love, death and the process of time. I do not claim it is an accurate perception but it is wholly presented as a vision. I know you all, I know your past, your present and future, yet I have not created you, I have merely "seen" you. All graduates in imposture perceive in this way. It is the reward or penalty for being no one; yet always there is no guarantee of truth. In an imposter, all points of view are burgled because the imposter has no point of view. Locked within the language of my imposture I further bind myself with every word I use, and yet I acknowledge the treasure of my deceit because it is within the human country of birth, meeting, parting, and death – the sanctuary of the imposter. And although the inevitable deceit also of language has built for us a world of imposture, we do survive within it, fed by the spark, at times by the fire of the recognition of the hinterland of truth.

'Complete imposture, I repeat, leads to nothingness in which one inhabits all worlds except the world of oneself.

'I am a literate person. I attended school, studied various subjects, read much and was not encouraged to question, until at the natural time of life when urgency arises, I, using the language, said Where, Why, How, Who, When, What? Indeed, at school I chanted a rhyme, a mnemonic:

I kept six honest serving men
They taught me all I knew;
Their names were Where and What and When
And How and Why and Who.

I questioned all replies, demanding proof, and proof came dressed in words, was identified by words; even the marvel of proof within music, painting, dancing, science, all art, came always dressed in words, while that mass of proof attainable only through the listening, watching heart, the language of feeling, that too became words, continuing to build the language of imposture.

'Perhaps I should not complain. We all inhabit the world. It is as natural to believe this as it is natural for us, standing on earth, to believe the earth is motionless, a secure foothold, although we have learned that it spins itself like a top observed as at rest within its spinning, surrounded by vapours of movement. We are all deep in imposture, surrounded only by intimations of truth; our foothold is not in truth.

'Do I appear to be writing a treatise? Let us enjoy our world until it and we come face to face with truth; our capacity for enjoyment is deep and not easily destroyed.

'I too have learned lately of the Gravity Star, the discovery of the star that annihilates the concept of near as near and far as far, for the distant star is close by, puncturing the filled vessel of impossibility, overturning the language of concept, easing into our lives the formerly unknowable, spilling unreason into reason.

'After this preamble let me begin. Do not be surprised to find yourself, your future, your past, within this small book. I'm writing of Kowhai Street, Puamahara, in the Maharawhenua. I have seized control of all points of view, although Mattina Brecon, the character from New York, trying to entice the point of view to herself, became unwilling to surrender it. I shall apportion it as I think fit because, as I have said, it is my only power, my true self that is no self. I speak now. I "tell". Generously I give the point of view to others. It is words that take charge of the telling. . . .'

Afterword

> And the belief that life is a dream and we the dreamers only dreams, which comes to us at strange, romantic, and tragic moments, what is it but a desire for the great legend, the powerful story rooted in all things which will explain life to us and, understanding which, the meaning of things can be threaded through all that happens? Then there will no longer be a dream, but life in the clear.
>
> (Christina Stead, *Ocean of Story*, 1986, p. 8)

The passages I chose to make up this anthology are grouped into three sections: Memories, Dreams, Reflections. These categories blur and overlap, however, in that certain preoccupations ebb and flow in the different tidal patterns of the textual tributaries we navigate towards their mouths that open on to the sea. Hence, my task of imposing *some* kind of shape or coherence on my selection was, paradoxically, impossible and relatively straightforward. Janet Frame's words, anchored by my framing devices, break free from their moorings in this new text, and drift, relocating themselves in other positions on the ocean of story. As they do this, their common features as vessels for particular voyages become more apparent. The anthologist's task of facilitating a recognition of the different qualities of the vessels then becomes in no sense a neutral one for, in choosing to select certain passages, a particular type of critical activity comes into play that intersects with what information or interpretation the anthologist chooses to supply or omit. Through particular juxtapositions of passages, and the sequential arrangement of the whole text, a particular reading of Frame's writing is being encouraged. Accordingly, taking account of this, and attempting to reduce its influence to allow more scope for the imaginings of you, the reader, this Afterword does not reflect the 'Memories, Dreams, Reflections' structure used to organise Frame's text(s) but, rather, invites you on to another boat from which we can hail passing vessels on the ocean of story.

Frame's account of the first thing she wrote is well-known: 'Once upon a time there was a bird. One day a hawk came out of the sky and ate the bird. The next day a big bogie came out from behind the hill and ate up the hawk for eating up the bird' ('Beginnings', p. 42). The three figures could be read as aspects of the self in interaction with language and the world. In *Living in the Maniototo*, her penultimate novel at the time of writing, the hawk stands in for language:

> . . . language in its widest sense is the hawk, suspended above eternity, feeding from it but not necessarily of its substance and not necessarily for its life and thus never able to be translated into it; only able by a wing movement, so to speak, a cry, a shadow, to hint at what lies beneath it on the untouched, undescribed almost unknown plain.
>
> (*Living*, New York, 1979, p. 43)

The self is continually constructed through language (here represented by the hawk), but the individual cannot control the way in which words are used in relation to her, let alone by her, to make sense of her experience. On the other hand, the poetic imagination (the bogie perhaps), can offer some degree of alternative power over the ways language is used to discipline and punish dissidents or outsiders. When Frame was encouraged to write about/against her own oppression or incarceration this offered a mode of resistance, a way perhaps of not being a bird at the mercy of others equipped to destroy it. The relatively powerless are deprived of speech; they live on

> [t]he edge of the alphabet where words crumble and all forms of communication between the living are useless. One day we who live at the edge of the alphabet will find our speech.
>
> Meanwhile our lives are solitary; we are captives of the captive dead. We are like those yellow birds which are kept apart from their kind – you see their cages hanging in windows, in the sun – because otherwise they would never learn the language of their captors.
>
> (*The Edge of the Alphabet*, New York, 1962, p. 302)

This is taken further in *The Carpathians*, where the inhabitants of a whole street in the town of Puamahara lose their use and understanding of language suddenly, in the middle of the night. They 'had each suffered a loss of all the words they had ever known, all the concepts that supported and charged the words, all the processes of thinking and feeling that once lived within the now shattered world of their words' (*Carpathians*, see p. 161). Letters from every alphabet fall like rain, settling 'now with a scab of dung, now with a cluster of jewels' (See p. 159).

A sustained meditation upon the possibilities and the limits of words, the power of language and its relationship to the material world, pervades Frame's work – 'I did receive the jewels I had been promised. I had opened the dictionary . . .' (*Daughter Buffalo*, see pp. 137–38). In *Living in the Maniototo*, Mavis has a discussion with her latest husband, Lance, about his vocational transition from French teacher to debt collector, not a positive move given Frame's argument about the importance of knowing language(s): 'Perhaps in future education programmes the concentration should be entirely on the learning of, first, one language, and then many? All other learning should follow' ('Departures', p. 94). Mavis laments the change Lance has made to his life:

> 'From the humanities, from language which never harmed anyone, to this!'
>
> Lance stared at me.
>
> 'You, of all people! Language that never harmed anyone. Ha, Ha. I've known more rape and murder and debt in language than there'll

ever be in Blenheim. Suicide too! This is what partly persuaded me to give up teaching language.'

. . . 'At least a novel doesn't prosecute or haunt anyone.'

'I wouldn't be too sure. And we both know, don't we, that the debt collector as well as the debtor can be haunted.'

'Of course.'

(*Living*, p. 59)

The way reality is mediated through words, often deceptively, is subtly exposed in Frame's writing. Milly Galbraith in *Intensive Care* has special spelling. She grows into 'a-doll-essence', she hopefully notices 'Amerrykins'. Later, she becomes a target for the fascist Human Delineation Act, which categorises and labels people, in this particularly brutal use of words, for survival or extermination. Milly is perceived as inferior, 'doll-normill', but she is aware of what is happening, declaring her intention to 'use my special spelling to make the words show up for what they really are the cruel deceivers' (*Intensive*, New York, 1970, p. 243). Margaret Dalziel suggests that such wordplay is: 'her creator's supreme expression of her own awareness of the beauty, danger and power of words . . . Milly's "own language" in its humour, pathos and horror, is not just a vehicle, but integral to the vision it conveys' (Dalziel, 1980, p. 38). Milly's 'special spelling' is a deliberate use of a variant of what was called in *The Rainbirds* the 'cold spelling'. In that novel, Godfrey Rainbird, after his brush with death, sees everything he reads as couched with menace; letters re-arrange themselves to connote threats that were not apparent in the un-reordered orthography. His address becomes: 'Dogrey Brainrid, of Feelt Drive, Resonsand Bay, Dunndie, Ogoat, Shuto Sanlid, Wen Lazeland, Rotusen he-mis-phere, the Drowl' (*Rainbirds*, Christchurch, 1960, p. 137).

Many of Frame's texts meditate upon language in other ways. The snowman, in the story of the same name, is baffled by the newspaper that has enveloped his head and blinded him: 'I can see nothing while I wear this torn newspaper over my head. I can only see words in print' ('Snowman, Snowman', see p. 121). The newspaper provides a delusive shelter from the dangerous sun. The snowman begins to see a little beyond the words that block his view, that seem to have hidden threats, when a bird (that dies soon afterwards) pecks a hole in the newspaper (see p. 123). The distorted spelling of the newspaper wrapped round the stone that Malfred Signal in *A State of Siege* clutches as she dies, again might be read as the impenetrability of words in yielding meaning – though also written on the newspaper is the appeal, 'Help, Help', a cry repeated by a number of Frame's characters. But the mysterious language that Malfred reads in the newspaper has been decoded by the critic, Judith Panny, as conveying images of birds preparing for migration and flying into the sky, evoking some sense of escape and freedom.

In 'Beginnings', Frame draws attention to the writer's fashioning of the raw materials of words into meaningful texts, in her suggestion of the semiotic and symbolic universes inhabited by her mother and father. The father has 'carefully hoarded grocery lists, greetings cards, notes, receipts, certificates, licences, telegrams, pages of financial plotting rich with ££££ signs, Art Union and Tatts tickets', while the mother has 'less disorganized' methods of controlling 'this devastating avalanche of words' (p. 41). The unreordered words in her father's collection of papers are subject to an attempted transmutation into art in the mother's 'trail of poem-spattered fragments', that provides in its turn the impetus for her daughters to write. When Frame writes, she is articulating, like Doris Lessing in *The Golden Notebook*, a sense of the chaos of contemporary existence that can nonetheless be made sense of to some degree by the attempt to describe it. Mark Williams relates an anecdote that shows James Joyce as doing something similar:

> As for Frame's so-called 'schizophrenia', it is sufficient to recall the words of C G Jung, the psychologist, who, when shown the diaries of James Joyce's daughter with the view that he should treat her, compared them to the seemingly 'schizophrenic' use of language in her father's novel *Ulysses*; 'she is falling, he is diving', he remarked.
>
> (Williams, 1990, 36)

This notion of diving recalls Adrienne Rich's image for the exploration of the unconscious in her poem 'Diving into the Wreck'. The ocean of story has at times unfathomable depths. Vessels lie on the sea floor, filled with various treasures for those who can descend there,

> First having read the book of myths,
> and loaded the camera,
> and checked the edge of the knife blade
> (Rich in Gelpi, 1975, pp. 65–66)

and return.

Frame later connects the traversal of the boundary between the conscious and the unconscious to travelling with relative ease between the material world and the Mirror City of the imaginary. The highly developed use of words and narrative structuring in Frame's work is so apparently artless and effortless that some readers think that she has fallen into it by accident or, at best, through (feminine?) intuition. C K Stead, for example, searching for a label for her writing suggests: 'Perhaps it needs some classification like "post-modern fiction" – but that would suggest an exercise in theories Frame is probably indifferent to. She works by instinct . . .' (Stead, 1986, 130). Ian Reid comments of *Intensive Care*: 'she seems unaware that baby-talk in itself is of little interest', and 'it's an unshapely book: too many longeurs, too much dispersal of energy' (Reid, 1972, 258). The many shifts of register of the narrating voices that Frame employs – from the prose poetry with which *Owls Do Cry* opens, to the parodic mode of Chicks' diary (See pp. 60–71) for example – have been read as naïveté, actual or assumed. They are perhaps better read as a highly self-reflexive and sophisticated metafictional strategy directed by Frame towards what she has called 'the wonderfully alive nerve of human curiosity which can yet be so easily touched, equally by the ordinary and the extraordinary recognitions' ('Departures', p. 87).

Frame's writing embodies a range of complex and profound philosophical, psychological and theoretical concerns worked through in a literary practice that has affinities with, but also differs greatly from Simone de Beauvoir's *She Came to Stay*,

Doris Lessing's *The Golden Notebook* or her *Children of Violence* sequence or, particularly in the case of *The Adaptable Man*, some of Iris Murdoch's novels. The philosophical depth of this other writing has been noticed and explored; by contrast, Frame has sometimes been cast in the role of naïve, even child-like girl-woman, a kind of female Peter Pan figure, unable or unwilling to 'grow up', and with a limited experience of life, as for example Ian Reid's comment in 1972 suggested:

> Miss Frame appears by now to have defined the territory of her imagination. It is not a large territory; indeed she has been virtually repeating the same story in novel after novel. Her work as a whole is remarkable for intensity rather than range.
>
> (Reid, 1972, 258)

The songs of innocence (and Blake is directly alluded to in *Owls Do Cry*), are not necessarily naïve narratives – and the same is true of fairytale. Frame reports the early appeal of Grimm: 'Any act was possible. Anything could happen. Nothing was forbidden.' ('Early Reading', 1975, p. 27). But much is in fact forbidden: when Francie in *Owls Do Cry* tries to play Joan of Arc, she ends up being burnt to death on the rubbish dump of former treasures. To stay only in the supposed safety of 'this' world, however, is to take hold of 'the wrong magic and the wrong fairytale' (*Owls*, New York, 1982, p. 39), and the result is that one ends up trapped in the 'satanic mills' or like Chicks, whose house is built on top of the rubbish dump, wondering: 'What if I have *no inner life*' (*Owls*, see p. 65). No real security from fear is offered by a tear-gas pen, a by-product of military technology, that can 'disable an attacker' (*Living*, see p. 140).

While reflection, or analysis, is not absent from Frame's work, it is rarely conspicuously foregrounded in comparatively didactic meditation such as is often found in Beauvoir, Lessing or Murdoch. Philosophical and psychological depths tend to be communicated in a simultaneously more concentrated and more diffuse way that has closer affinities to some of the poems of Sylvia Plath or the allegorical *Dreams* of Olive Schreiner.

Abstract thought is not absent, but it is not separated from the intuitive:

> The proper place for abstractions is in a region of the mind which must be entered in nakedness of thought. Certain abstractions are powerful and may be lethal yet the way to approach them is not to carry weapons of personification but to act as soldiers do when they surrender, to discard all the known means of defence and retaliation and walk naked toward the hostile territory.
>
> ('Snowman, Snowman', see pp. 120–21)

I read Frame's work as embodying a search for true knowledge that would place her at some remove from the poststructuralism whose preoccupations she might seem to prefigure. 'I forgot the rebel in the eye, the illusions that can point the way to truth' (*Siege*, New York, 1966, p. 71). As Judith Panny comments: 'It is indeed both amusing and ironical to hide allegorical depth and significance in a text that affects a postmodern superficiality and playfulness' (Panny, 1992, p. 179). Her book argues that:

> Allegory and the postmodern mode share one significant area of common ground. In both, language is wielded self-consciously; both ask the reader to pay attention to the work as a text, rather than as a story, or as a study of a character. Furthermore, postmodernism's lack of inhibition has allowed Frame's sense of humour free rein.
>
> (Panny, 1992, p. 180)

Despite the high level of philosophical and metaphysical reference and speculation that can be read into Frame's work, its richness also partly lies in its subtle engagement with political questions that arise in the course of material existence in the world, issues such as those of gender, sexuality and race. Anger about sexually abusive fathers – as in *Intensive Care*, where Tom Livingstone takes on for his daughter the colossus-like qualities of Sylvia Plath's Daddy: 'his huge foot in its dead-leaf boot stuck in the sky' (see p. 155) or about doctors carrying out the rape-like invasion of electro-convulsive therapy is communicated through savage but controlled satire:

> – Turn on, my love, he will say, and reach for the switch, and caress the red luminous eye with his gentle hand.
>
> (*Owls*, see p. 87)

It is true to say that Frame, like Patrick White, Virginia Woolf, and Keri Hulme in *The Bone People*, has in general little interest in the detailed depiction of sexual encounters. Sometimes, homosexual relationships are represented, as they are in *The Edge of the Alphabet*, and in *Daughter Buffalo* – though Patrick Evans prefers to read the latter as 'another parable about the predicament of the artist, the dying old man Turnlung representing Frame's New Zealand self, perhaps, and the young man, Edelman, a new, cosmopolitan self capable of fathering rough but authentic beasts that are not quite what we expect to come from human beings' (Evans, 1985, p. 380) – except within Greek legends of mirrors, mazes and Minotaurs, he might have added. But sexual relationships in Frame's narratives seem usually out of the question because of their potential risk:

> But the price of wool! The cost of the warmth has always been too great. I know, who lived outside fiction where the cold wind blows across the waste spaces from heart to heart.
>
> (*Living*, see p. 175)

In Frame's account, in the third volume of her autobiography, of Easter in Andorra, an ambivalent desire to belong within the rural family is represented:

> Oh why could I not be there, too, in the painting? I, in spite of my Celtic red hair, my birthplace an Antipodean world where the trees like the pines of Andorra, were a serious evergreen, the colour of eternity, of sovereignty, of the forest ruling naturally with the sea, the sky, the land, the weather. My desire to belong (and how much closer may one be to belonging when one is within both the real city and the Mirror City?) increased my willingness to allow others to decide my life.
>
> (*Envoy*, see p. 109)

But the attraction of the life of an Earth Mother figure is limited; counterposed, as for many other women writers earlier and contemporaneously, to what would be lost in assuming such a role.

> I felt a chill alarm spreading through me at the prospect of my future life, first in Andorra, then in the south of France working in vineyards, or helping in the fur shop, perhaps living in poverty, trying to take care of *los crios* . . . I did not want to become one of the characters that I had seen so romantically as living figures from the paintings of the great artists. Nor did I want to repeat what I had now done several times – use poetry to put myself in human danger and to try to force a flow of love towards me. I was learning that the uses of poetry are endless but not always harmless. (*Envoy*, p. 108)

For many of the male protagonists, any expression of their sexuality is inextricably bound up with the First or Second World Wars. *Intensive Care*, in particular, deals with this. Tom Livingstone, since the War, has carried with him a dream of 'a woman who had spread so wide in his world, for so many years that she had sucked up his life as the sun sucks up the sea and all the streams and rivers . . .' (*Intensive*, see p. 150). But when he finds this woman in the hospital for the aged she is 'the image of an old tart with dyed hair, a life-sized doll mechanised to cry out in pain every few minutes, to groan in the night, to whisper her pleas for morphine. The Ciss Everest Cancer Doll. . . . Miss World War I' (*Intensive*, see p. 151).

In *A State of Siege*, in Malfred's encounter in the fernhouse with Wilfred, soon before he is to sail off to the War, it is a diseased sexuality that pervades this Garden, in which the ferns end up 'spattered' with white 'mildew' (see p. 72). Malfred later recalls this incident rather differently, as having been a profound experience, offering some physical connection to another person:

> we made love in the fernhouse, and I did not, as I need to remember that I did, turn Wilfred away or mock him but I loved him with my

> body and with my thoughts. It is hard to find words to describe it, for it has been described so many times with the eye of the writer looking at or away from the object; it has been described in trite or simple ways, as in the Biblical *He knew her, she knew him*. I cannot think of it in this way. Nor can I say dramatically, 'Here in the fernhouse I surrendered to him, we were one.' I have seen and heard all these phrases and none is right and clear, none is exact.
>
> (*Siege*, pp. 205–6)

This passage may offer a partial explanation for Frame's unwillingness to give detailed depictions of sexual encounters.

One conspicuous absence in Frame's work, perhaps even a limitation of its vision, is representations of the Maori population indigenous to Aotearoa. She mentions in parentheses in 'Beginnings' that her 'step-great-grandmother was a full-blooded Maori' (p. 41), and the narrator of 'The Lagoon' tells us: 'When my grandmother died all the Maoris at the Pa came to her funeral, for she was a friend of the Maoris, and her mother had been a Maori princess' (see p. 25). But in most of Frame's writing, Maori are almost invisible, glimpsed briefly in the distance. In *Owls Do Cry*, Amy Withers remembers how while she and Bob were courting, 'they met the old Maori running from the ghosts;' (see p. 34). Malfred in *A State of Siege* sees 'two families of children, Maori and Pakeha, playing near the swamp' (*Siege*, p. 61).

Malfred expresses a desire for the access that one of her pupils seemed to have to Maori legendary knowledge, denied to her and to other Pakeha:

> It wasn't fair that they should know so much, instinctively, about their country; that, when they looked at the sky, they might think, without self-consciousness, of Rangi, while Malfred's image seemed a poor secondhand one of Gods reclining on clouds, eating lotus and hurling thunderbolts.
>
> (*Siege*, see p. 146)

The sense of exclusion of the colonising culture from the history of the land is conveyed here though, interestingly, Malfred expresses this in the metaphor that she previously rejected for sexual connection: 'Malfred realized that her envy of Lettice Bradley had concealed an envy of all who had "known" in the Biblical sense: he *knew* her,; she *knew* him – the myths and legends of the Maori who "knew" the land' (*Siege*, p. 125). Perhaps a resistance to simplistic appropriation can be read in such passages, and some Maori critics have read Frame this way. Powhiri Rika-Heke has commented on how:

> To date, literary texts show clearly that we, the Maori, remain part of the tension of an indigenous consciousness for the Pakeha. But it is neither the contemporary Maori nor a truly historical one that remains, but rather a romanticised historical artefact. Thus the white culture attempted to incorporate the Other, rather superficially, through referring to Maori place names, to Maori legends, ceremonies, 'putting kowhai, puarangitoto, manuka, rata, tarapunga on postage stamps,' or selling Maori carvings, faked or genuine.
>
> (Rika-Heke, 1993, 91)

While Maori characters remain almost entirely absent, at least until *The Carpathians*, Judith Panny has shown that there is increasingly widespread reference to Maori mythology and names in Frame's later writings. However, they are often mixed with European etymologies.

> While Maniototo means 'plain of blood' in Maori, the Latin meanings combine to suggest 'total madness' . . . By her contrary perspective Mavis [in *Living in the Maniototo*] mocks Brian. Her ironic stance is comparable to that of the little black fantail, the piwakawaka of Maori mythology who laughed aloud at the half-god Maui's attempt to vanquish the Death Goddess Hine-nui-te-po. Awakened by Piwakawaka's laughter, the Goddess crushed her would-be assailant. We are reminded of this myth when, in Blenheim, a little black fantail accompanies the ghost of the suburb's famous poet. A typically cryptic allegorical image, the black fantail links the creative writer not only with the song maker of Frame's very first tale, but with the artist's disenchanted view of human arrogance.
>
> (Panny, 1992, p. 144, p. 155)

In such moves, the distinctive authority of Maori myths in their own country can become subsumed into a kind of universalised collective unconscious that removes their distinctive relationship to *their* place. In *The Carpathians*, Frame uses 'invented Maori names' (Panny, p. 160). There seems to be an almost assimilationist wish in Mattina's (not unironically narrated) expectation that New Zealand will be 'small enough for everyone to be neighbours; a family place . . . With everyone, all races, sharing the Memory Flower (*Carpathians*, London, 1988, p. 60).

An exception to the general absence of Maori characters in Frame's writing is the chapter from *The Carpathians* above (see pp. 191–98), but Mattina's outsider status as an American woman is implicitly that of the whole New Zealand Pakeha culture; the earlier part of the chapter suggests: 'the Maoris were the people of the land who held or harboured a source of memory which the latecomers, the other immigrants were only now learning to seek and share' (see p. 205). Frame is, as I read her, ambivalent about this seeking and sharing that many Pakeha in Aotearoa have recently been attempting to engage in, and some of the problematics of it emerge in the episode of Mattina's visit to the marae community in *The Carpathians*.

In a recent interview with Marion McLeod, Frame talks about her current view of inter-racial interaction in Aotearoa:

> Frame has bought some books on the Maori language and is very interested in the immersion courses that are now available. She's encouraged by the resurgence of interest in Maori language and legends. 'There has always been interest, yet too often it has been the interest of the living directed towards the presumed dead. I think it is marvellous and good that, however slowly—too slowly—the people banished to sleep, to a silence that equates with death, are alive, speaking and writing their own language and sharing its riches.'
>
> (Interview 1988, 26)

* * *

Memories, dreams and reflections reconstruct and deconstruct themselves through Frame's work. Memories are modified with the passing of time: 'In times of suffering memories are formed that as the years pass have the capacity to spread under the seismic impact of their own stress causing other memories to disappear and new details of the time, newscapes to reappear in the present' (*Carpathians*, p. 65).

Dreams can be consoling or menacing or, simultaneously, both. *The Rainbirds* concludes with a meditation, looking out at the sea from the land, in which dreaming is an activity that is dangerous, where the order imposed upon the world through ceaseless activities that attempt to maintain normality (often in Frame's writing, the day-to-day labour of women – in housework, gardening, maintaining the family) can be shattered:

> you can sit in the sun on the low rock wall surrounding the grave and look at the ocean breakers rolling in, or you can close your eyes and dream, but do not dream too deeply in case, awakening, you discover that the yellow and gold flowers, geraniums, marigolds, nasturtiums, snapdragons, all that Beatrice planted and tended during her weekend visits to the grave, have merged one with the other, have changed their warm bright yellow and gold to become a floating mass of red lilies.
>
> (*Rainbirds*, p. 206)

Here the reassuring warmth and brightness of the yellow flowers – 'Wallflowers along the clay bank, taking a warm glowing hold/ with suncolour' ('Sunday Drive', see p. 89) – transmutes into a pool of blood. At bleak times, memory has to be drawn upon to recreate the dream:

> but this is only if you visit in summer; if you go there in winter you will have no help with your dreams, you will have to experience for yourself the agony of creating within yourself the flowers that you know will blossom there in summer.
>
> (*Rainbirds*, p. 206)

Reflection, both in the sense of meditating upon and imaging the world, works with both memory and dream. Mirrors become a motif of increasing importance in Frame's later work – though the title of her first book of poems, *The Pocket Mirror*, introduced this notion in terms of a small personal reflection. The sense of a separate self that is developed through the acquisition of language with which one differentiates between one's own subjectivity and that of an other, is sometimes referred to as passing through a mirror stage. Encounters later with mirrors in Frame's writing can represent transformations of the self, as when the loss of a finite identity is experienced by Toby Withers:

> He looked for a mirror which would show himself, Toby Withers, his distinct identity; but in all the images he stared at, he was nowhere to be found . . . Why had he surrendered the right to be himself? Why had the mirrors given him the terrible responsibility of being other people? He had been driven from himself as a rabbit is driven from its burrow, and here he was now, unprotected, unhoused, like a rabbit alone under a sky of circling hawks, of hungry identities preying upon him.
>
> (*Edge*, New York, 1962, pp. 292–93)

In *The Carpathians*, the loss of a sense of an individuated separate identity is a positive thing for Dinny Wheatstone, the 'imposter novelist', who suggests: 'my imposture . . . as a result of my nonentity, is accompanied by an uncanny perception of human life, love, death and the process of time. I do not claim it is an accurate perception but it is wholly presented as a vision . . . It is the reward or penalty for being no one; yet always there is no guarantee of truth' (see p. 205). This situation is perhaps analogous to that of the bogie, with greater power than the hawk, with the ability to journey to the is-land. To be able to pass backwards and forwards through the mirror, communicating about the dream city of the imagination, able to cross without fear from 'this' to 'that' world, can be important for the creative artist. Malfred, who has taught representational art for forty years, knows that she has resisted this:

> Malfred knew that she was on no human terms with the 'room two inches behind the eyes,' that what lay there, treasure or no treasure,

> did not belong to her, had not been captured by her and given a name.
>
> (*Siege*, p. 9)

Repeated journeys to Mirror City feed the creative imagination that can invent, even if only in words at first, alternative futures.

> Remember your visit there, that wonderful view over all time and space, the transformation of ordinary facts and ideas into a shining palace of mirrors? What does it matter that often as you have departed from Mirror City bearing your new, imagined treasures, they have faded in the light of this world, in their medium of language they have acquired imperfections you never intended for them, they have lost meaning that seemed, once, to shine from them and make your heart beat faster with the joy of discovery of the matched phrase or cadence, the clear insight.
>
> (*Envoy*, pp. 175–6)

The rather mysterious Envoy is a kind of go-between or guide, connecting the world of imagination (of which dreams are a part) and the everyday reality re-membered into art. The 'Mirror City before my own eyes' (*Envoy*, p. 176), is perhaps both reflections and reflecting, and the journey to the City needs the special skills of the ship's pilot: 'A contemporary ingredient in the cauldron world of the witch-novelist is a pilot's thumb' (*The Adaptable Man*, New York, 1965, p. 3). On such voyages a great alertness is necessary. In *The Envoy from Mirror City*, as the narrator travels on a boat from New Zealand to Britain, she thinks of her fellow passengers: 'if I'm to be and stay a writer I must follow all the signs in everything they say and do, and in their silence and inactivity, reading their face and the faces and the eyes that are mapped with their private isobars and isotherms above the fertile lands, the swamps secret with marsh birds, the remote mountains sharp with rock formations, softened with snow. I must forever watch and listen' (*Envoy*, p. 7). Actual voyages to other places neither offered Frame an escape from societies dominated by capitalism, patriarchy and militarism, nor produced any major changes in the nature of her writing produced in that different context. The Canadian writer, Alice Munro, while visiting Britain, said of Frame's stories:

> They are so good for me right now because they're so very un-English. They have that quality of openness and risk and abandonment of control which I'm just hungry for. She never loses it completely but she's right there on the edge.
>
> (Munro, 1987, p. 86)

The role of 'witch-novelist' in the position of outcast, and whose vision remains uncannily intense, is not a comfortable one. Complacency, even contentment, is impossible, as the parody of Yeats' poem 'The Lake Isle of Innisfree' (*Maniototo*, see pp. 198–200) perhaps suggests. The witch has powers, but also the potential for being ostracised. Frame is not tame:

> Witches still have a tough constitution; there's a kind of unselfishness, detachment in their devilish cooking. They can't eat it themselves. What do they eat? Maybe they feed on each other. Life on a heath with thunder and lightning, mixing a cauldron of uneatables for others to observe, admire, shrink from, is not much fun. But who wants fun?
>
> (*Adaptable*, p. 3)

In an interview in 1977, Frame plays ironically with notions of possession:

> To write a book . . . one must have deep feelings and be haunted by something . . . You must be excited and see the whole thing. That vision of the whole sustains you through the writing although at the end the original theme may be unrecognizable. A book is an accumulation of hauntings.
>
> (Frizell, 1977, p. 7)

At the same time, the vision has to be rendered into words that make *some* kind of sense, 'that bind with their spell' ('Beginnings', p. 42) or, as Mercer puts it, give us 'a spell from the spell(ing) of convention, which might induce dizzy spells in the reader but ultimately prove spell-binding' (Mercer, 1994, p. 148).

While Frame engages with difficult and demanding material there is also a pervasive ironic humour, wit and irony – as Yeats put it, a 'gaiety transfiguring all that dread' – that makes the voyaging always exhilarating and, for her non-Antipodean readers perhaps especially interesting, in the light of the prognosis in this passage from *The Carpathians*:

> There was now, however, another wave often more hoped for and talked about than real, but visible in the land itself, flowing from the land and having been there for centuries concealed often by the more visible waves from elsewhere. It was now flowing in its own power, inwards and outwards, reaching the shores of the Northern Hemisphere.
>
> (*Carpathians*, p. 82)

LIST OF SOURCES

Part One: Memories

1 'The Lagoon', from *The Lagoon and Other Stories*, Christchurch: Caxton Press, 1951, pp. 7–11.
2 *To the Is-Land*, London: The Women's Press, 1983, pp. 73–5.
3 *Owls Do Cry*, New York: Braziller, 1982, pp. 24–30.
4 *To the Is-Land*, London: The Women's Press, 1983, pp. 76–83.
5 *Scented Gardens for the Blind*, Christchurch: Pegasus Press, 1963, pp. 41–47.
6 *Intensive Care*, New York: Braziller, 1970, pp. 107–120.
7 *An Angel at My Table*, London: The Women's Press, 1984 pp. 40–5.
8 *Owls Do Cry*, New York: Braziller, 1982, pp. 120–4 and 126–132.
9 *A State of Siege*, New York: Braziller, 1966, pp. 136–8.
10 *Faces in the Water*, New York: Braziller, 1961, pp. 184–198.
11 *Owls Do Cry*, New York: Braziller, 1982, pp. 55–9.
12 'Sunday Drive', from *The Pocket Mirror*, London: W H Allen, 1967, pp. 12–17.
13 *The Rainbirds*, Christchurch: Pegasus Press, 1969, pp. 98–103.
14 *The Envoy from Mirror City*, London: The Women's Press, 1985, pp. 60–4.
15 *The Envoy from Mirror City*, London: The Women's Press, 1985, pp. 82–9.

Part Two: Dreams

16 'The Day of the Sheep', from *The Lagoon and Other Stories*, Christchurch: Caxton Press, 1951, 52–8.
17 *Snowman, Snowman: Fables and Fantasies*, New York: Braziller, 1963, pp. 1–2 and 75–82.
18 *Snowman, Snowman: Fables and Fantasies*, New York: Braziller, 1963, pp. 159–170.
19 *Daughter Buffalo*, New York: Braziller, 1972, pp. 92–97.
20 'The Clock Tower', from *The Pocket Mirror*, London: W H Allen, 1967, pp. 1–2.
21 *Living in the Maniototo*, New York: Braziller, 1979, pp. 78–9.
22 *A State of Siege*, New York: Braziller, 1966, pp. 8–10 and 121–5.
23 *Intensive Care*, New York: Braziller, 1970, pp. 13–14, 15–17, 18–19 and 20–25.
24 *The Carpathians*, London: Bloomsbury, 1988, pp. 125–30.

Part Three: Reflections

25 'My Last Story', from *The Lagoon and Other Stories*, Christchurch: Caxton Press, 1951, pp. 121–3.
26 *The Adaptable Man*, New York: Braziller, 1965, pp. 45–6.
27 *Living in the Maniototo*, New York: Braziller, 1979, pp. 222–230.
28 *The Envoy from Mirror City*, London: The Women's Press, 1985, pp. 93–105.
29 'Dunedin Story', from *The Pocket Mirror*, London: W H Allen, 1967, pp. 48–50.
30 *The Carpathians*, London: Bloomsbury, 1988, pp. 81–7.
31 *Living in the Maniototo*, New York: Braziller, 1979, pp. 114–115.
32 *Daughter Buffalo*, New York: Braziller, 1972, pp. 41–2 and 57–9.
33 *Intensive Care*, New York: Braziller, 1970, 196–7.
34 *The Carpathians*, London: Bloomsbury, 1988, pp. 51–2.

FULL BIBLIOGRAPHY OF THE WORKS OF JANET FRAME

The Lagoon and Other Stories, Christchurch: Caxton Press, 1951, 2nd ed. 1961; Random Century, 1990.

Owls Do Cry, Christchurch: Pegasus Press, 1957, 2nd ed. 1958; New York: Braziller, 1960; London: W H Allen, 1961; Melbourne: Sun Books, 1967; New York: Avon, 1971; Auckland: Hutchinson, 1985; London: The Women's Press, 1985.

Faces in the Water, Christchurch: Pegasus Press, 1961; New York: Braziller, 1961; London: W H Allen, 1962; New York: Avon, 1961; London: The Women's Press, 1980.

The Edge of the Alphabet, Christchurch: Pegasus Press, 1962; New York: Braziller, 1962; London: W H Allen, 1962.

Scented Gardens for the Blind, Christchurch: Pegasus Press, 1963; London: W H Allen, 1963; New York: Braziller, 1964; London: The Women's Press, 1982.

The Reservoir: Stories and Sketches, New York: Braziller, 1963.

Snowman, Snowman: Fables and Fantasies, New York: Braziller, 1963.

'Memory and a Pocketful of Words', *Times Literary Supplement* (June 1964): 487.

The Adaptable Man, Christchurch: Pegasus Press, 1965; New York: Braziller, 1965; London: W H Allen, 1965.

'Beginnings', *Landfall* 19, 1 (1965): 40–47.

The Reservoir and Other Stories, Christchurch: Pegasus Press, 1966; London: W H Allen, 1966. (The stories in this edition were selected with the help of Dr Margaret Dalziel from the two US volumes, *Snowman* and *The Reservoir*, 1963).

A State of Siege, New York: Braziller, 1966; Christchurch: Pegasus Press, 1967; London: W H Allen, 1967; Sydney: Angus and Robertson, 1982; Australia: Sirius, 1989.

The Pocket Mirror, New York: Braziller, 1967; London: W H Allen, 1967; Christchurch: Pegasus Press, 1968; London: The Women's Press, 1992.

The Rainbirds, London: W H Allen, 1968; Christchurch: Pegasus Press, 1969; published in the US as *Yellow Flowers in the Antipodean Room*, New York: Braziller, 1969.

Mona Minim and the Smell of the Sun, New York: Braziller, 1969.

Intensive Care, New York: Braziller, 1970; Wellington: Reed, 1971; London: W H Allen, 1971; Wellington: Century Hutchinson, 1987.

Daughter Buffalo, New York: Braziller, 1972; Wellington: Reed, 1973; London: W H Allen, 1973; Auckland: Century Hutchinson, 1986; London: Pandora, 1990.

'Early Reading: Janet Frame on *Tales from Grimm*', *Education* 24, 9 (1975): 27.

Living in the Maniototo, New York: Braziller, 1979; Auckland: Hutchinson, 1981; London: The Women's Press, 1981.

'Departures and Returns', in G Amirthanagayam, ed. *Writers in East-West Encounter*, London: Macmillan, 1982.

You Are Now Entering the Human Heart, Wellington: Victoria University Press, 1983; London: The Women's Press, 1984.

To the Is-Land (Autobiography 1), New York: Braziller, 1982; London: The Women's Press, 1983; Auckland: Hutchinson, 1984; London: Grafton, 1987.

'A Last Letter to Frank Sargeson', *Islands*, 1, 1 (1984): 17–22.

An Angel at My Table (Autobiography 2), New York: Braziller, 1984; London: The Women's Press, 1984; London: Grafton, 1987.

The Envoy from Mirror City (Autobiography 3), Auckland: Hutchinson, 1984; New York: Braziller, 1984; London: The Women's Press, 1985; London: Grafton, 1987.

The Carpathians, New York: Braziller, 1988; Auckland: Hutchinson, 1988; London: Bloomsbury, 1988.

Janet Frame: An Autobiography [combines the three volumes of autobiography], Auckland: Century Hutchinson, 1989; London: The Women's Press, 1990.

CRITICAL BIBLIOGRAPHY

Note: This selective list includes only commentators referred to in the Preface and Afterword. It also includes the interviews with Frame cited there or, in one case, included in the text. A recent full and accessible bibliography of writing about Frame can be found in Delbaere's *A Ring of Fire*.

Alley, Elizabeth, Interview with Frame, 28 April 1983, Radio New Zealand.

Alley, Elizabeth, selected and ed. *The Inward Sun: Celebrating the Life and Work of Janet Frame* (Sydney: Allen and Unwin, 1994).

Broughton, W B, ' "With Myself as Myself": A Reading of Janet Frame's Autobiography', in Delbaere, ed. *Bird, Hawk, Bogie*, 221–32.

Dalziel, Margaret, *Janet Frame* (Wellington: Oxford University Press, 1980).

Delbaere-Garant, Jeanne, ed. *Bird, Hawk, Bogie: Essays on Janet Frame* (Aarhus: Dangaroo Press, 1978). Revised edition, *A Ring of Fire: Essays on Janet Frame* (Aarhus: Dangaroo, 1992).

Dowrick, Stephanie, 'Janet's Pen Triumphs Over Scalpel – An Interview with Stephanie Dowrick', *Sydney Morning Herald* (23 November 1985): 45.

During, Simon, 'Postmodernism or Postcolonialism?' *Landfall* XXV, 3 (1985): 366–80.

Evans, Patrick, 'Janet Frame and the Art of Life', *Meanjin* 3 (1985): 375–83.

Ferrier, Carole, ' "The Death of the Family" in Some Novels by Women of the Forties and Fifties', *Hecate* II, ii (1976): 48–61.

Ferrier, Carole, 'Dualities and Differences Revisited: Recent Books on Janet Frame', *Hecate* XX, ii (1994): 251–59.

Freidan, Betty, *The Feminine Mystique* (Gollancz: 1963).

Frizell, Helen, Interview with Frame, 'Janet Frame, NZ's Shy Genius', *Sydney Morning Herald* (19 December 1977): 7.

Hulme, Keri, Interview with John Bryson, *24 Hours*, Supplement, January 1994.

Jung, Carl Gustav, *Memories, Dreams, Reflections*, recorded and edited by Aniela Jaffé, trans. Richard and Clara Winston (New York: Vintage, 1965).

Kidman, Fiona, 'Another Letter to Janet Frame', in Alley ed. *The Inward Sun*, 67–73.

Lévi-Strauss, Claude, *The Raw and the Cooked*, (New York: Harper and Row, 1969).

McLeod, Marion, Interview with Frame. 'Janet Frame in Reality Mode', *NZ Listener* (24 September 1988): 25.

McLeod, Marion, 'The Language of the Is-Land', *Listener* (8 October 1990): 102.

Mattei, Anna Grazia, 'Exploring the Is-Land', in Alley, ed. *The Inward Sun*, 175–81.

Mercer, Gina, 'Exploring "the Secret Caves of Language": Janet Frame's Poetry', *Meanjin* XLIV, 3 (1985): 384–90.

Mercer, Gina, *Janet Frame: Subversive Fictions* (St Lucia: University of Queensland Press, 1994).

Minh-ha, Trinh, T *Women, Native, Other* (Bloomington: Indiana University Press, 1989).

Munro, Alice, 'Strong Mood', Interview article by Marion McLeod, *Listener* (29 August 1987): 86.

Panny, Judith Dell, *I Have What I Gave: The Fiction of Janet Frame* (Wellington: Daphne Brasell Associates, 1992).

Reid, Ian, 'The Dark, the Dull and the Dirty', *Australian Book Review* (Autumn 1972): 258.

Adrienne Rich's Poetry, B. Gelpi and A. Gelpi, eds. (New York: W W Norton, 1975).

Rika-Heke, Powhiri, 'Second World Margin: Indigenous Writing in Aotearoa. "Don't Tell Us Who We Are": Maori Women Define Themselves Through Their Writing', NZWSA Conference Papers, Auckland: 1993.

Roberts, Heather, *Where Did She Come From? New Zealand Women Novelists 1862–1987* (Wellington: Allen and Unwin, 1989).

Scott, Rosie, Interview with Laurel Bergmann. *Hecate* XVIII, ii (1992): 33–45.

Stead, C K, *In the Glass Case: Essays on New Zealand Literature* (Auckland: Auckland University Press, 1981).

Stead, Christina, 'Ocean of Story', *Ocean of Story: The Uncollected Stories of Christina Stead* (Harmondsworth: Penguin, 1986).

Wersba, Barbara, 'On Discovering Janet Frame', in Alley, ed. *The Inward Sun*, 163–65.

Williams, Mark, *Leaving the Highway: Six Contemporary New Zealand Novelists* (Auckland: Auckland University Press, 1990).

Wilson, Janet, 'Postmodernism or Postcolonialism? Fictive Strategies in *Living in the Maniototo* and *The Carpathians*', *Landfall* 11 (1993): 114–31.

The Women's Press is Britain's leading women's publishing house. Established in 1978, we publish high-quality fiction and non-fiction from outstanding women writers worldwide. Our exciting and diverse list includes literary fiction, detective novels, biography and autobiography, health, women's studies, handbooks, literary criticism, psychology and self help, the arts, our popular Livewire Books for Teenagers young adult series and the bestselling annual *Women Artists Diary* featuring beautiful colour and black-and-white illustrations from the best in contemporary women's art.

If you would like more information about our books, please send an A5 sae for our latest catalogue and complete list to:

The Sales Department
The Women's Press Ltd
34 Great Sutton Street
London EC1V 0DX
Tel: 0171 251 3007
Fax: 0171 608 1938

Also of interest

Janet Frame
Owls Do Cry

Janet Frame's first novel remains a classic of contemporary literature. The story of the growing up of the children of an educated but impoverished family, *Owls Do Cry* reveals the extraordinary qualities that characterise Janet Frame's later work: her joy in the power of words; the sense of paradox that colours every moment; and the haunting of the present by the ghosts of past and future.

'A kind of personal archaeology, painstaking and intensely felt.' *Times Literary Supplement*

'Chilling and poetic.'
Jane Campion, director of *An Angel at My Table* and *The Piano*

'Her voice is both poetical and practical...Words remain Frame's saving grace, her *raison d'être*, and her defiance.'
The Times

Fiction £5.99
ISBN 0 7043 3958 7

Janet Frame

Faces in the Water

'I was put in hospital because a great gap opened in the ice floe between myself and the other people whom I watched. I was alone on the ice . . . I was not yet civilised. I traded my safety for the glass beads of fantasy.'

Faces in the Water is a novel as wide and deep and unexpected as madness itself. It is about confinement in mental institutions, about the fear the 'sane' have of the 'mad' and the ways in which that fear banishes and punishes those whose reactions to a truly cruel and insane world is to move into a world which is self-centred.

'One of the most impressive accounts of madness to be found in literature . . . A masterpiece.' Anita Brookner

Fiction £6.99
ISBN 0 7043 3861 0

Janet Frame
Living in the Maniototo

With wit and a magnificent command of language, Janet Frame offers us a richly imagined exploration of unchartered lands. Our guide through the Maniototo is a woman of multifold personalities: Violet Pansy Proudlock, ventriloquist, also known as Alice Thumb, gossip, and as Mavis Furness Barwell Halleton, a writer who has borne children and buried husbands. Under their guidance, we learn firsthand about the necessities, deceptions and dangers of the creative process – on which our own survival depends...

'As near a masterpiece as we are likely to see...A novel full of riches.' *Daily Telegraph*

'Puts everything else that has come my way this year right in the shade.' Norman Shrapnel, *Guardian*

Fiction £6.99
ISBN 0 7043 3867 X

Janet Frame
Scented Gardens for the Blind

Vera is the mother who has willed herself sightless. Erlene, the daughter, has ceased to speak. And Edward, husband and father, has taken refuge in a distant land.

In this brilliant, haunting and sometimes hilarious novel, Janet Frame explores the boundaries and inner landscapes of family life. *Scented Gardens for the Blind* makes magic with language, dazzles the imagination, and forces us to face the reality of loneliness and the possibility of hope.

'Lyrical, touching and deeply entertaining.'
John Mortimer, *Observer*

'A brilliant outburst of a book.' *Kirkus Reviews*

Fiction £6.99
ISBN 0 7043 3899 8

Janet Frame

You Are Now Entering the Human Heart

These dazzling stories, selected by the author herself from all her published and unpublished work, bring together the very best of Janet Frame's short fiction over a creative span of forty years.

From impressions of an impoverished rural childhood to life in some of the world's largest cities; from the sardonic to the deeply compassionate; and from striking realism to the haunting resonance of dream and fable, this superb and moving collection confirms Janet Frame's position as one of the world's finest writers of fiction.

'The country's greatest writer of fiction since Katherine Mansfield.' Bronwyn Dorreen

'An extraordinarily direct and original voice.' *Literary Review*

'A constant delight.' *Daily Telegraph*

Fiction £6.99
ISBN 0 7043 3938 2

Janet Frame
The Pocket Mirror

Vivid, playful and compelling, *The Pocket Mirror* is the only published poetry collection from one of the world's most accomplished living writers.

Internationally acclaimed for her award-winning novels and autobiographies, this deeply personal and evocative collection reveals Janet Frame to be a poet of insight, diversity and consummate skill.

'She has shown, so quietly, a mastery of the English language which dazzles one beyond ordinary praise.' Naomi Mitchison

'Everyone should try Janet Frame in one form or another.' Rachel Billington, *Financial Times*

Fiction £7.99
ISBN 0 7043 4331 2

May Sarton
Journal of a Solitude

The intimate accounting of her life as a writer, *Journal of a Solitude* instantly tripled May Sarton's dedicated readership and remains her bestselling, best-loved book. Here, Sarton tells of the hard work and discipline involved in 'cracking open the inner world' and shares the joy and satisfaction when, after a long struggle, 'the sonnets come'. A classic of the genre from one of the greatest diarists of our time.

'A book rich in perception, wisdom and charm.' *Herald*

'Sarton has always been, in the most fruitful sense, a transgressor of boundaries: of geography, of time, of gender, and of genre...But it is in the journals that her considerable literary skills find fullest scope. She can be a poet, novelist, political commentator, and moral philosopher in an art form she has made very much her own...Sarton has made her distinctive literary mark, and it is here that her reputation will endure.'
Janette Turner Hospital, *The Sunday Times*

Autobiography/Memoirs £7.99
ISBN 0 7043 3969 2

May Sarton

A Reckoning

Told that she has only months to live, Laura decides she will do her dying her own way. Searching for the 'real connections' in life she finds herself drawn deeper and deeper into 'what it is to be a woman'. For it is with women that Laura finds the real connections to have been...

'An exciting, exhilarating, radiantly vital account...May Sarton's finest.' *Plain Dealer*

'The novel has an intensity and an essential truth which will make it an enduring bestseller.' Carolyn Heilbrun

'A warm and uplifting book that will almost certainly gladden rather than sadden the reader.' *Options*

Fiction £6.99
ISBN 0 7043 3939 0

May Sarton
A Reckoning

Told that she has only months to live, Laura decides she will do her dying her own way, searching for the real connections in her life. She finds herself drawn deeper and deeper into what it is to be a woman. For it is with women that Laura finds the real connections to have been...

'Absorbing, exhilarating, passionately vivid account... [illegible]' [illegible]

'The novel has a rhythm and an essential truth which will make it an enduring best-seller.' Carolyn Heilbrun

'A warm and uplifting book that will almost certainly [illegible] rather than sadden the reader.' Options